THE DAYS OF OFELIA

BY GERTRUDE DIAMANT

The days of Ofelia

Illustrated by
John O'Hara Cosgrave II

1942
The Riverside Press Cambridge

HOUGHTON MIFFLIN COMPANY · BOSTON

The Riverside Press
CAMBRIDGE · MASSACHUSETTS
PRINTED IN THE U.S.A.

THEY worshipped a goddess of the earth who was also the goddess of the corn, and they called her by a name which means: that which sustains us.

CLAVIGERO: ANCIENT HISTORY OF MEXICO

AMONG their foods the first place must be given to corn, the grain which Providence granted to that part of the world in place of the wheat of Europe. With corn the Mexicans make tortillas, or round flat pancakes, a bread which is different from that of Europe in taste, shape, and in the manner of making it. The Mexicans and all the other peoples of that vast part of the world had the custom of eating tortillas, and to this very day it is their custom.

CLAVIGERO: ANCIENT HISTORY OF MEXICO

Contents

THE DAYS OF OFELIA

Atoyac 82

THE street behaved just like a river. It rambled through empty lots and circled a field of corn, and then it disappeared. There was a high white wall where it disappeared, but not a sign or a person to tell me where the street had gone. Presently a boy on a bicycle came by, and seeing me standing in perplexity, he waved and called: 'Follow the wall.' I followed it, and there was the street again.

I was looking for Atoyac number 82, where the morning paper said there was a furnished apartment — cheap, comfortable, decent, ideal for an American. And I was in that part of Mexico City where all the streets bear the names of rivers. Already I had crossed the Tiber, the Rhine, and the River Po, old favorites familiar from high-school days. But what of the River Atoyac? Nobody knew where it was, and nobody seemed to have heard of it. The sun was high and the sidewalk burned my feet, and I wandered on, hoping that the street would not disappear again. For I was carrying the two big valises which I had brought with me to Mexico, and which now contained all that I owned in the world.

It was a way of burning my bridges behind me. I was tired of living in boarding-houses (those beautiful old colonial mansions of the guide-books) with their damp dark rooms, slippery floors and dreadful furniture. I had vowed never to enter another old colonial mansion, but to leave them all to their decaying splendors and to the Spartan Mexicans. And if there was no place in the city with an easy-chair and a comfortable bed and dry and sunny, then I would go back to the States. But I did not want to go back, either. There are three hundred thousand Otomí Indians in Mexico, and I had tested a mere one hundred. I must test another two hundred at least to prove — but no, it is not scientific to know in advance what one is going to prove.

I put my valises down, flexed my arms and looked around. There were houses now, but not a sign to tell me if I had come to the River Atoyac. To know where you are in Mexico City, you must look at the corner houses; and with luck you will see a tiny plaque which bears the name of the street. But usually it isn't there at all, and the Mexicans have a sweet reasonableness when they cannot enlighten you. 'Pues ... you see, señorita, the signs are missing which should bear the names of the streets. So I cannot tell you, señorita, forgive me.' It was Sunday and the stores were closed and the street deserted. I left my

valises standing and walked until I came to where a man
was sitting on the curb. He looked up from under a wide
sombrero. 'No, señorita,' he said, 'really I cannot tell you.
I have little time here.' 'Time!' I thought scornfully.
'What time do you need to tell me the name of a street?'
And then I remembered my still meager Spanish. It is an
idiom meaning that one has only just come to a place. 'But
if you ask the señor at the little stand over there,' he went
on, 'possibly he can tell you. He has much time here.' So
I crossed to the little stand.

'Atoyac!' mused the man of much time. 'Atoyac!' He
smiled engagingly. 'Forgive me, señorita, but I am unable
to say. I do not concentrate on the names of the streets.
However, if you should wish for the Street of the River
of the Plata' — he pointed with an exquisite grace — 'it is
over there, señorita, just two blocks over there.' 'Thank
you,' I said, 'I do not wish for the Street of the River of the
Plata.' And I went back and gathered my valises and
wandered on. There were empty lots again and many
blocks where the houses were still being built. Soon I
would come to the city limits. I could see fields of corn
and beyond them the mountains, splendidly luminous in
the afternoon light. But at the last corner before the
fields began I came to a house that miraculously bore the
number 82. Five little girls sat on the doorstep.

'Is there a furnished apartment here?'

They chorused raggedly, pointing. 'Arriba ... upstairs.'
And I saw that they all had the same shade of brown-green
eyes. Then they rose in a body and we all went up.

I could not tell in that mass of brown arms and legs and

serious faces that escorted me upstairs which one was
Ofelia. But at the top of the stairs one child detached herself, took a bunch of keys from under her apron, and turning, waved her hand at the others with a royal gesture,
as who should say: 'Away, O profane ones! Efface your-
selves.'

The other little girls turned as one man and slunk down
the stairs again, submissive as lambs. Then she of the keys
opened the door. 'I have such trouble with them, señora,'
she said, sighing. 'They are very presuming children. I
alone am supposed to show the apartment, but they always come up with me. If you should wish to see it again,
please ask for Ofelia. Ofelia Escoto at your service.'

But I knew in one glance that I had found my home. It
must have been the casement windows that decided me,
and the way the rooms made a corner so that I could spy
on myself, a nice diversion for one who lives alone. And
there were two 'closts,' rare in any Mexican apartment,
and I would not have to go to the market to buy those
hideous guarda-ropas, which come from the time of the
Count of Monte Cristo. Ofelia must have noticed my
pleased expression, for she ran to the window. 'Ramona,
Lupita, Cristina, Elodia,' she called. 'Run and call father.
The señorita will speak to him.'

There was a chorus of sí's and the sound of a stampede,
and I gathered that the herd had been waiting obediently
under the window for just such a signal. Presently Ofelia's
father came, followed by all the children, who now entered
fearlessly as under a higher authority. Señor Escoto had
very blue eyes. It was the first thing you noticed about
him, and the thing you would always remember about him.

It was a deep blue, untamed and challenging, and when he
looked at me sideways and smiled with the very white
teeth that Mexicans have, I found myself thinking, inev-
itably, 'Handsome devil.' Only his smile was soft and
lazy, and I liked him because it contradicted the fierce
blaze of his eyes. It was very easy to arrange things with
him, because all he did was to smile and say softly, 'Yes,
that can be arranged.' Meanwhile the children stood by
with their hands behind their backs, and I thought how
there must have been a Scotch ancestor, perhaps far back,
who had given them their name of Escoto. But the Scotch
blue had skipped the children, or at least it had compromised with the Indian black to give them those bronze,
brown-green eyes.

Ofelia was the last of the children to go, and Señor
Escoto waved her away with the same imperious gesture
she had used on her little sisters. 'Señora, you must forgive me for Ofelia,' he said earnestly. 'Do not let her
bother you. She is a very presuming child.'

Then they were gone. Only the door opened again, and
Ofelia put her head in. 'Señora,' she whispered sibilantly,
'when you wish for a maid, remember me. Ofelia Escoto,
at your service.' She closed the door lingeringly and I
turned back to the apartment. But the windows drew me,
flooded with a blue so clear that I had to go and look down
on the lot below, to make sure I was not floating through
space. The Escoto children were playing there, and from
somewhere came the music of a harmonica and the sound
of metal clinking, over and over again. At the far end of
the lot men were playing a game, tossing a little piece of
metal into a cupped stone. It was late, yet the day still

lingered, the long golden Mexican day which seems as though it could never die. In the morning it lifts the spirit, but in the late afternoon, when the air is saturated with golden light and unmoving as if it had stopped breathing, one feels a great sadness — the weight of time, a premonition of eternity. That sadness I felt now, looking out on the lingering day while it grew dark in the apartment where I was not yet at home, and very much alone. And because I did not want to feel that sadness I quickly unpacked the valises and spread the intelligence tests on the desk. And very soon I was checking and adding and dividing, figuring I.Q.'s for the Otomí Indians.

Skulls — Two for Five

IN MEXICO you must have a maid if you wish to be considered a person of consequence. Someone who does the washing on the roof, while she sings at the top of her voice and the sun makes splendid ebony of her hair, and who bargains with the butcher and who fetches your tortillas, and goes to market for you. I had no maid and so I did the marketing myself, going out every morning with a basket and a bag swinging from my arm. It was the wrong thing to do. In the corner grocery Manolo and his wife, leaning elbows on the counter, gave me good morning as I passed; but their eyes followed me disapprovingly, and I am sure they thought: of these Americans any queerness may be expected.

But how could I explain to them my great delight in

going to market, or tell them that it was circus and holiday, theater and fair and folklore to me? The market of
the Merced is on the other side of town, a long bus ride
from Atoyac 82. But I preferred it because it is such a
large market, a city in itself where one can wander and
get lost. And it has infinite variety — green glass from
Monterrey, and baskets from Toluca, and sombreros from
every state in Mexico; and sandals hanging from the stalls
like meats being cured, and leathers and cloths from
Tlaxcala, besides every fruit that grows in Mexico, and
every herb for medicine or witchcraft.

You cross the Great Plaza and go east, in the direction
where the volcanoes show on a clear day; and even before
you come to the market there are covered stalls, and the
cries begin. 'Buy, marchante, choose! What were you
looking for, what did you desire?' A marchante, I take it,
is one who marches around presumably looking for a bargain. 'What do you need, marchante, what will you carry
home? A bargain, a bargain, take advantage!' It is an
endless litany, soft and cajoling. 'Buy, my little blonde
one, buy, my pretty one! I bring oranges from Córdoba,
let's see if they please you.'

Then comes the market proper — the difficult walking
between the stalls, the dusty air and the slippery dirt, the
smell of tortillas frying in bubbling fat, and the smell of
leather and grass mats still green; and the din of strolling
musicians and the whine of beggars, and the cries of the
cargadores bent double under huge bags of produce, blindly
charging through the crowd. 'Make way! Make way!'

The church where the prostitutes come to pray to their
patron saint is near the market, where the stalls end in a

slum more terrible than any in Mexico City. But before you come to the church there is a chapel, where the women come to spend a moment out of the sun, and to say some prayer that they have in mind. It has a terrifyingly realistic Christ who sits leaning forward, the beads of blood bright on his waxen cheek, and one pale hand uplifted in the twilight air. I remember the chapel because I took refuge there on the Day of the Dead. I had made the mistake of going out bareheaded on a clear day and very soon I felt dizzy; for the Mexican sun is no pleasant benediction like our northern sun, but a fierce stroke of consuming light. Still, I did not want to turn back. The gleaming gay skulls, sugary-white and with splendid gold trimmings, lured me on, and I walked farther and farther into the market, bewitched by the cries of the women. 'Skulls, skulls — two for five.' I thought of buying a skull and having my picture taken, holding it in the crook of my arm like some medieval alchemist. Nobody would have thought it strange, on that day, if I had wandered through the city carrying a skull. For the whole city is given over to death, and there is feasting in the cemeteries and everywhere there are dancing skeletons, and pastries and candy take the shape of skeletons as naturally as our gingerbread takes the shape of Santa Claus. You cannot even open the paper without seeing skulls. All the famous men from the president down are pictured with fleshless grins, and someone writes very nasty epitaphs for them. It is a day for morbid joys and gruesome delights, for death casts its jigging ribaldry over everything.

But not a day for walking in the sun. I was beginning to feel sick from the smell of burning copal, the incense of the ancient Aztecs, with which they perfumed the stench of their human sacrifices. And the skulls no longer stayed in the stalls, but began to rise and float around me like balloons, and I felt myself rising too, and all of us jigging like motes in a sunbeam to the cry of 'Two for five, two for five.' Somewhere, I thought, there must be shade, where I can find reality again and escape from these white skull-bones. But there was no shade, only the merciless sun, chalk-white on the awnings over the stalls, sugar-white on the skulls that floated around me.

I saw brown hands molding cool ices of a poisonous febrile pink, and brown hands extended strange fruits to me with seductive cries. 'Buy, my pretty one. Buy, my little blonde one.' But they were the ices and fruits of death, sweet and poisonous, and I floated past them and smilingly rejected them with a wave of my hand. At which the skulls that floated with me also smiled; for while they were thus cheated of me for a time, at least I continued to suffer a fiery thirst, and that pleased them. I remember in particular one skull with the name Guadalupe beautifully inscribed on her white forehead in red icing. I had seen her first in a stall with some other female skulls — Ramona, Esmeralda, and Eusebia; and she seemed to have joined my floating escort and taken the lead, a merry wench if a bit unfleshly.

It must have been high noon, for there was no shade anywhere, and I longed for a church, a dim Christian interior to absolve me from the sun. There, I knew, the skulls must disappear, for clearly they were demons of the fierce Mexican sun and in the dark they could not exist. By now I had come to the slum, and beggars stretched

SKULLS — TWO FOR FIVE

their stumps of arms toward me, and the lazars, the blind and the maimed streamed past me, phantasma stepped out of some medieval painting. The buildings too were fantastic. They leaned gently awry, sinking into the earth. *Mexico is built on a filled-in lake, and old buildings with poor foundations sink slowly into the swampy ground.* It was a nice cool note to remember from the guide-books, and I hoped it was so. For if not, I was quite mad. But I remembered also what one of the Spanish conquerors had written: that the stench of human sacrifices in the Aztec temples was so great that his nostrils could not abide it. Surely that blood-thirst of the ancient Aztecs had not died out, but still claimed its living victims. I was convinced of it and already imagined the headlines: GRINGA DIES OF SUNSTROKE IN THE MERCED MARKET. And then I came to the chapel and went in, and leaned against the cold marble wall, while the air whirled around me and whirled the waxen Christ, with his pale hand lifted in reproof. The women there had put their market bags aside to kneel and pray, but they looked at me slyly while their lips moved. They were all decently shawled in long black rebozos. And as I went out one of them said to me, gently rebukeful: 'Yes, one must cover the head.'

Whenever I went to market Ofelia watched me. The Escotos lived in a hut on the lot next to the house, and I had to pass it to take the bus. One day she waylaid me.

'Señora, you are going to market,' she said, respectfully accusing. 'I too wish to go.'

Since in dealing with children precedent is everything, I at once said no very firmly, and then thought of all the reasons for it. I was in a hurry, the market was far away, there would be heavy things to carry.

'I will help you carry them,' she said.

'No, there's a little boy in the market who helps me.'

'Ah, señora,' she sighed. 'Those rascals. They are shameless ones. They carry little and charge much. I will carry your things without payment. And as for the fare...' She showed me a ticket she had found, good for one ride on the bus. 'I have that too.'

'It is not the fare,' I said.

Her eyes filled with tears. 'But I long so to go.'

'What for?'

'To buy something that pleases me.'

'And what pleases you?'

'I don't know, señora. How can I tell? I would have to go to the market to find out.'

'Then why don't you go?'

'There is no one to take me.'

'And your mother never goes?'

'Never, señora. There is no occasion for it, because she lacks the money to buy things.'

'And your aunt, the young and pretty one?'

'She too lacks the money. Besides, she says the market is very dirty.'

'Yes, it is very dirty.'

'But so many things! Ay, señora, what a mountain of things!' And she looked off into the distance, as if she could see the market and all its wonderful variety.

I had to give myself for vanquished, as the Spanish says. 'Come,' I said, and took her hand.

We did not return from the market until dark, for so

many things pleased Ofelia that she could not make up
her mind. We had explored all the stalls before the choice
narrowed — a pair of blood-red earrings, or the blue cotton drawers, both for thirty centavos. She bought the earrings with money she had earned carrying tortillas for the
Señora D'Arce in the house. 'But I am not her maid,' she
reassured me, 'and so should you need me, señora . . .'

After that I never went to market alone. I would wave
my bag when I stepped out of the house, and Ofelia came
flying like a bird to the signal, and took the bag from me
and off we went together. She insisted on carrying it even
when it was full, swinging it up to her shoulder. And when
we came home the spoils had to be disgorged at once, and
we would congratulate ourselves on the cheapness of this
or that, or deplore the high cost of something else. And
there were always new fruits to savor, which Ofelia chose
for me. She watched, very distraught, while I tried them,
as if the future of the whole species depended on my ver-
dict. But I liked everything except the mangos, which
have a musky rich after-taste not for my simple palate.

Very soon Ofelia began to hint that it would be a fine
thing if I would let her go marketing alone. 'A fine thing
for you, señora,' she said. 'Then you could sit at your desk
all day without interruption.'

'But your mother would never let you go so far alone,'
I told her, distractedly trying to concentrate on the intelligence tests.

'Pues, it is far,' she admitted, 'but then if I were really
your maid . . .'

'Child! You are too young to be a maid.'

'Oh no, I am ten. And my sister Aurora, who bears very

few years more than I, already has employment. If you would only speak to my mother . . .'

She leaned on the desk and looked with her head on one side at the drawings made by the Otomís. Problem: it is raining, draw the object which you use to protect yourself from the rain. Only it doesn't rain in the Valley of the Mesquite where the Otomís live, and the problem is how to get water, water to drink and water for the soil.

Ofelia nudged me gently. 'Señora, if you would only speak to my mother . . .'

I had seen her mother often, but never spoken to her. She was tall, much taller than Señor Escoto, and in her long black skirt and black rebozo sheathing head and shoulders she looked like some figure from mythology. Whenever she met Señor Escoto on the street one could imagine that Fate herself had accosted him for the final reckoning. And usually he took a few coins from his pocket and reluctantly gave them to her. But one night Mrs. Escoto knocked at my door. In Mexico when you open the door to a neighbor, you must at once bid him come in, come in, whether you know him or not. Never let him stand on the threshold, for the Mexicans consider it a dangerous and unhallowed place. So I bade Mrs. Escoto come in, and she apologized profusely for coming in, and it made a fine chorus all the way to the living-room.

'You must forgive me, señora, for disturbing you,' she began, 'but it's about this Ofelia here. She is a very presuming child. I have such trouble with her.' Ofelia had come in too, and stood with her hands behind her back, watching me intently from under her long lashes. 'She says you have taken her for your maid and that I am to buy her an apron.'

'Why, no, we only go to market together.'

'There, you see?' Mrs. Escoto turned wrathfully on Ofelia. 'The señora does not confirm your story. It is another one of your lies. Just imagine, we have not enough to eat in the house and I was to go out and buy her an apron! Go!' — she waved Ofelia away. 'Go, presuming one! You are not wanted here.'

Ofelia went out slowly, looking back at me with a beseeching urgency in her eyes, and I found myself saying, 'But now that I remember — yes, we did talk of her being my maid. But not about the apron, of course. I will buy that for her myself.'

'Go!' Mrs. Escoto waved again, fiercely unsatisfied until Ofelia had quite disappeared. And then, to cover a change of mood, she rearranged her rebozo and smiled at me. 'Ay, señora, the trouble I have with these children. One never knows what to believe. And they are growing up so wild, so wild here in the city. We are not of the city, señora. We are of Jalisco, from the pueblo of Atotonilco near Guadalajara. And we came here of necessity, so that we might live and have a shelter over us. Such a shelter as it is! In our pueblo it would have served for the beasts.' She sighed and looked around. 'But here you are in glory, with such a wealth of things. In our little house in Atotonilco we too had a table and chairs and a bed, all that which makes the felicity of life. Ay, señora, what pleasure it is to have many things, many things as you have here.'

'Yet more than I need. Being alone ...'

'And look you, now we have two daughters to go out and work as servants. The sadness of it. Two daughters to be serving-maids. Aurora, who is thirteen, she already has employment, and Ofelia. Ofelia is ten. And what I wanted to ask you — what I came to find out — señora, could you give her a little salary, just a tiny little salary?'

In Mexico the diminutive is so common, for flattery, for wheedling or for sheer adornment, that one never knows whether to take it seriously or not. So I felt called upon to explain. 'It will have to be a tiny little salary in all truth. I could not give the child more than ten pesos a month.'

A purr of satisfaction escaped Mrs. Escoto before she shook her head. 'Yes, that is little, to be sure. But then Ofelia is young, and as yet of little use.'

'And she will eat with me.'

Mrs. Escoto smiled deprecatingly. She had strong white teeth, but her gums were covered with red sores. 'Ah, no, señora, I was not thinking of that. There is always something to eat in our house. Not much, but a mouthful can always be found.'

'She will eat with me,' I insisted. And, as if the little salary had expanded visibly, Mrs. Escoto instructed me sternly: 'And set her to work on her knees. Do not spare her, not for a moment. For she must learn, she must learn her trade which is that of a serving-maid. Because look you, señora, we are not young — I and her father. I have a little one, Lolita — perhaps you have seen her? She can hardly walk yet, but for all that we are not young, we are well advanced in years. It is only that one goes on having children until the thing finishes itself. And if, God forbid, they should one day be left orphans ... She rose after a while, fatefully tall, and adjusted her rebozo and smiled at me. She had a gaunt prettiness, but it was ravaged by time and illness, and I thought there was something very sad about her. 'And forgive me, señora, that I came to disturb you. But the child bothered me so ...'

While we were preparing the supper that night, I asked Ofelia: 'What do you eat in your home?'

'Pues —' She hesitated only because the answer seemed so obvious to her. 'Pues,' she said, 'we eat tortillas.'

'Yes, but what do you have for breakfast?'

'Tortillas.'

'And for lunch?'

'Tortillas.'

'And for supper —'

'We do not eat supper, only Daniel and my father, because they are men. But Daniel is not here now and so it is only my father. He eats the tortillas which are left over.'

'And are there many left over?'

'It depends. You see, my mother gives me a peso in the morning and I buy two pounds of dough, and with it my mother and my aunts make the tortillas. Two pounds is not much, señora, and they finish quickly.'

'Yes, I see.'

'And then we are twelve, counting my little grandmother and my two aunts. There's my Aunt Delfina, her husband has left her, and my other aunt who is very ill.'

'But do you never have anything else?'

'Pues, sí! We have black beans from time to time, and eggs when my Aunt Delfina goes to her village, which is Saint Pedro of the Pines, to fetch them. And meat on Sundays. But it's never very good meat. Just imagine, señora, we pay the butcher thirty centavos for a piece of meat, and it's pure nerves. My father says it's a shame. And we have coffee, too, but my father says it is bad for one. Is it so, señora?'

'Oh yes, coffee is bad.'

'My aunt, the older one, cannot sleep when she drinks coffee. But then she is very sick, and the pains keep her awake too.'

I asked what the sickness was, and Ofelia shrugged and said, 'Quién sabe? ... who knows?' Spoken like a Mexican, who never says 'I don't know,' with its ring of personal responsibility. But he says 'who knows,' and he says it with a great weariness, as if the thing in question were utterly unknowable, or as if it would be asking too much of him to find out.

I Feel Like an Aviator

So OFELIA became my maid. Dear Ofelia! How ardently you craved the martyr's crown, and begged to be set sweeping and scouring and scrubbing on your knees. And how busy I was, keeping you busy, lest you suffer a moment's idleness and so fall from grace. I wanted to dismiss you a hundred times in those early days, but I couldn't. Because it would have been an expulsion from paradise for you, because your new maidhood was seventh heaven and a crown of glory to you.

And how patiently in those early days you listened to my wisdom, the well-fed wisdom of my race, of which I delivered myself while we sat eating the raw carrot — telling you of the wonderful vitamin and other magical entities. You listened patiently but without belief; and

yet you grew bright-eyed and rosy-cheeked, and different
from your little sisters who were waxen and pale as the
very tortillas of their diet. 'We shall turn into horses,' I
observed once, as we sat munching our raw carrots. 'Or
into burros,' you said, and then you turned serious. 'Yes,
señora, there are people who remain burros all their lives.
Those who have never been baptized in the Holy Church.
All their lives they never have the wisdom of human
beings.' You were old, Ofelia, with the ancient wisdom of
the Church; and old with the ageless dignity of the rebozo
that framed your face. And only when you looked long-
ingly at the ugly little celluloid dolls in the market did I
remember your scarce ten years. Mornings, when I drew
the curtains aside and looked down on the lot, I saw you
standing at the door of the hut and braiding your hair.
Already you had been to church. You had risen at five,
weary and dirty from unrestful slumber on a straw mat,
and unwashed but decently sheathed in your rebozo, you
had walked many blocks to hear a Mass in the great golden
church on the Reforma.

And now, your peace made with God, you were preparing for the secular duties of the day. You braided your
hair without a mirror. It was long chestnut hair, which
the Mexicans call blond, as they call any hair blond which
is not of an Indian blackness. No doubt the Scotch ancestor who gave you your name also gave you your chestnut hair. But your skin was for Mexico — dark dark.
When, obeying my orders, you scrubbed your face, you
looked at yourself in the mirror and said despairingly,
'But I am dark dark, just the same, señora.' And you
hated your dark skin, because everyone knows that true

beauty is white as the driven snow. And after you had braided your hair you went into the hut and came out wearing your black rebozo — the coarse cotton one, for the silk one was only for church — and with a basket on your arm and a peso in your hand, the single peso that must buy the day's food, you went to market for the pound of dough and for my paper. You did not understand why I must have another paper every day. 'Haven't you yesterday's?' you asked. And then I explained that the news is created fresh every day; and after that, with lofty understanding, you asked each morning as you gave me the paper: 'And what is the news today?'

'Well, Mexico is going to elect a president.' Or, 'The war in Europe continues.' You did not know that Mexico had a president, or that there was a place called Europe. These were faraway things of no importance. But on the other hand, all the saints were near, and you knew the days of each and how one must honor them; and you knew what is mortal sin and what is forgivable. And you knew how to bargain in the market-place, and how to pound chile and make tortillas — things adequate for your world.

And you knew also how to behave in difficult circumstances. For I believe it is a difficult circumstance to sit down at table with one of a strange race, to eat strange foods. That first time we sat down at table together — you did not touch the food and I wondered why you sat so quietly without eating. And then you said, with great dignity and with that Mexican way of half-statement: 'I, señora, as I do not eat at table ...'

'But eat any way you like,' I said. And you fell to, tearing the meat with your hands. But you did that also with reserve and a certain dignity.

And you knew the gracious courtesy, the wonderful politeness of your people. 'Well, señora, I am going,' you said when the day's work was over. But you lingered. 'With your permission, señora.'

'Well, señora, until tomorrow,' and now you were at the door, where you waited a decent moment. 'Well, señora, until we meet again. May it go well with you.' And then the door closed softly, and your 'Adiós, señora,' floated back to me. And thus, at the end of each day you left me, for leave-taking is a delicate matter, and one must never go abruptly.

Dear Ofelia! You kept me so busy that my Otomís languished without their I.Q.'s. And I had to work far into the night, and I was tired with the altitude and dozed over the papers. And so I would put them away with nothing done, and go to bed, and sleep was only a small moment before the sun sprang up from the mountains, and I heard the women making tortillas — the steady slap-slap as they tossed the dough between their palms.

It is the sound of Mexico, as the blue of the sky is its color. And the cold of the mountain night is still in the air when it begins. I would rise and draw the curtains, and see the sun low and clear on the level white buildings. From the huts came a haze of smoke and the morning noises — chopping of wood, water splashing, and the pigs squealing; and Ofelia's little sister singing shrilly over and over, 'To heaven, to heaven let me go, to receive the blessed crown, the blessed crown.' And through it all the insistent slap-slap of tortilla-making, a rhythmic sound like part of a ceremonial, and one seems to hear far off the accompanying beat of feet in some primitive dance.

I could see the women working in the smoky huts where the night still lingered, their hands twinkling in the obscure light, their faces bronze and shadowy as if emerging from a dark canvas. Outside the men were washing, dousing their heads in the dirty water in the barrels; and then, drying their faces, they went into the huts to eat. They squatted on the dirt floor, and took many tortillas at a time, and folded them and downed them with black coffee. All the men of the huts worked on the houses that were being built on the block; and after breakfast they strolled over to the foreman's shack, a leisurely stroll with hands in pocket and much jesting. 'Ay, how lonely I was last night!' It was the sung-out complaint of one of them — no doubt a bachelor; and every morning the men laughed at it, standing in front of the foreman's shack, and singing back retorts that increased the laughter. For singing is the word for Mexican speech. It is most noticeable in the working people, when they call to each other, talk loudly or jest. Then something happens to their speech — a lilt at the end of each phrase, a musical cadence always the same, with the last note fading away sweetly resonant. I used to think there was an opera company under my windows, for it was not speech that I heard, but a recitative always straining to break into song.

The roll-call was always a long and elaborate business, and I am sure that the first step in bringing the Mexicans up to our northern standards of efficiency must be to shorten their names. 'Señor Ildefonso Sánchez Morales.' 'Señor José Herrera Rodríguez.' The foreman intoned each name with long-drawn sonority, and each man answered, 'Presente, maestro.' Then the men who had come

from other parts of the city went into the shack and hung
up the woven bags in which they carried tortillas. But the
foreman more often than not stands frowning at his list.
'Juan! Juan!' he calls into the shack. 'Are you drunk
again?' Everyone looks toward the shack and Juan comes
out, and he is drunk again. And grinning happily and
waving his arms as if he were flying. No doubt he had
been in the cantina a few blocks away, which bears the
name: I Feel Like an Aviator.

Ofelia calls the men who work on the buildings 'los
peones,' the peons. This used to be the term for the serfs
on the large estates before the Revolution. But now,
either with land of his own or the right to acquire it, the
rural laborer of Mexico is called a campesino — a peasant
or farmer. Yet the word peon still persists, both for the
rural laborer and the hired hand of the city. Nearly all
the men who work on the buildings come from the prov-
inces. They are not men of the city, not skilled builders.
They have only recently been on the land, and the planting
of a field of corn is more familiar to them than the processes
of brick and mortar and the plumbline. Perhaps that is
why the hammering on the buildings sounds much busier
than it really is; for the men work at their own rhythm,
very relaxed and slow about whatever they are doing. And
if a peddler passes they all stop work, looking on while one
of their number drives a bargain, at great length and with
sallies of wit.

There are always peddlers coming to the street. There
is the old man who trots along under a perilous tower of
painted straw chairs. He has to trot very fast to keep
them from falling. And the Indians come with flowers

from Xochimilco, and with berries and herbs. And a man and a woman come driving a small herd of goats before them. They are very young goats, uncertain on their legs, and they stop stupidly before no obstacle at all. Then the man and the woman scold them in an Indian language which is probably Aztec. They are both very small, and ragged and barefoot, yet somehow proud and indomitable in their rags. The man's hair is a matted black mass under his sombrero, but the woman's two braids lie like carved wood against the high cheekbones. And there is a woman who comes selling live chickens, their dangling heads showing more life than the baby she carries on her back, half suffocated in her rebozo. And there is a man who comes flailing a flock of turkeys, that invade the street like mummers with their cries and strut and color. And work must stop and everyone must watch while one of the peons buys something, for a good bargain is a public concern. And why should there be haste to make a building that will be only two stories high? Of course, building a sky-scraper is different.

But the women really worked. They washed clothes every day, though the only water they had was carried from the buildings in old gasoline cans. I used to watch, and marvel at the way they treasured every drop of water, at their intricate system of wringings and rinsings that turned the clothes out as spotless as if a whole ocean had cleansed them. Mexican women always wash clothes horizontally on a stone, working their arms back and forth, instead of up and down. Perhaps it comes from the prac-tice of washing clothes on a river bank, or because they have grown so used to moving their arms that way from grinding corn on the metate. But in any case it is certainly contrary to gravity, and very hard work. And it would be a good thing if the feminists who agitate for communal mills to grind the corn would also ask the Government for hundreds and hundreds of washboards. Then, when the clothes had been hung on the fences to dry, the women aired the sarapes and the straw sleeping mats. And then all the earthenware pots were scoured with great wads of coarse hay, rinsed and turned upside down to dry. In the sun their burned bottoms gleamed like ebony.

Ofelia and I worked also — the morning warfare against the flea. For it is ironical that in the high Valley of Mexico, where the mountain forms bespeak cosmic geologic upheavals, the greatest menace to man is the tiny flea. Let every resident of Mexico City put pesos for 'fleet' on his budget. Fleet (the American Flit) is the name that Mexicans have adopted for any insecticide. You may buy a Mexican brand of fleet, but my grocer did not advise it. 'Yes, señorita,' he said, 'I recommend the American fleet, even though it be dearer. The American product truly kills. The Mexican merely stuns the animal.' And he gave a fine imitation of a stunned flea. Ofelia loved spraying fleet. The smell of it enchanted her, and she would go around inhaling it as though it were perfume.

Ofelia could not tell time, but she went by the sound of the hammering. When it ceased altogether, she would announce: 'Las dos, señora. Two o'clock' — very proudly, as though she had looked at the clock. Then the peons invaded Manolo's store, calling loudly for beer and soda pop — the busiest hour for Manolo, who never took a siesta. The men who did not live on the lot ate in the scant shade of the buildings; but the others ate in the huts — tortillas not so fresh as in the morning, and perhaps a paste of black beans fried in lard. I would hear Mrs. Escoto calling Ofelia's little sisters for this, their last meal of the day. At night there would be no supper call to take them from their playing. Yet they would play in the darkening air with tireless energy, and with no knowledge that they were hungry. Only they were thin and bony, and waxen as the image of the Virgin that stood on a packing-case in the hut.

Ofelia called them her little pigs. 'Pues, I am not hungry any more,' she would say, laying down the knife and fork which she now used with some facility. We would agree that it was a sad waste of food to throw away what was left on her plate, and, since she had been talking about her tierra and the ranch where they used to live, she would suggest casually: 'I could feed it to my little pigs.' Which continued the talk and allowed her to carry off the food without embarrassment. 'Tierra' literally means earth, and thus the Mexican designates the region from which he comes, the place of his birth and childhood. Ofelia loved to talk about her tierra, like all good Mexicans, though she never seemed sure whether they had owned their ranch or whether it had been part of a great estate. But she said there were abundant fruits there, wood to be given away, oranges ripening faster than they could be picked, and eggs at two centavos in near-by Atotonilco. Yet they left their tierra and came to the city.

'But why?' I asked.

'Well, my father came first.'

'Yes, but why did he leave the ranch?'

She considered. 'Pues ... you see, señora,' and her words gathered aggrieved momentum, for she remembered now exactly how it had been. 'They paid him only fifty centavos there on the hacienda where he worked. Imagine that! Only fifty centavos for so much work every day, and for the family that we are, too. It was unjust, wasn't it?'

'Certainly it was unjust. But still you were better off there than here, weren't you? You had everything to eat, and a real house, and beds to sleep on ...'

'Yes, señora, but we went barefoot all the time, and my father was angry that they paid him only fifty centavos.'

'And now?' I asked, looking down at her torn shoes.

She sighed. 'Now there is no money for shoes, either. Still, it is better that we came. My father earns more, oh, much more. It's only that we are so many — so many of us.'

She feels so sure that it was better, yet I cannot quite understand. Perhaps they did not own the land after all, and the abundance was none of theirs, but only a charity from a kind hacendado. Or perhaps they did own the land, only that it gave them a surfeit of fruits where there was no one to buy, and what good is abundance if one cannot see a silver peso from one year's end to the next? Or perhaps it was simply as she said: 'My father got angry that they paid him only fifty centavos.' A man may well get angry at that and feel himself worth more, and leave everything he has to prove it.

'Still,' I reasoned, 'why didn't your father, when he found work here, send money back to the ranch? Why did all of you come to the city?'

'My father wrote us one day to come, and we came,' she

said, with the air of one who gives more than adequate reason. And then with even more conviction, 'Nor did we wish him to be alone here in the city.'

I had to let it go at that, though I was still troubled; for it seemed to me that they had made only an illusory change. They were still barefoot and poor as they had been before, and now they were starving too.

'And doesn't your father ever think of going back?'

'Well, no' — she considered. 'My mother talks of it often, but without much purpose. And the city is better, señora. Just imagine, in Atotonilco the streets are so narrow that an automobile could not pass through them, that is, if ever one came.'

'Just imagine.'

'And besides, my brother Daniel is coming now. He stayed behind so as not to forsake his sweetheart. But now they are going to get married and they are coming here for the nuptials. And Daniel will work and we will have more money.'

And more mouths to feed, I said to myself, thinking how little simple mathematics counted with them. 'And will Daniel and his sweetheart sleep in the hut?'

'Pues, sí. My father wishes it.'

'And won't you be rather crowded?'

She did not think so. 'What does it matter,' she sighed, 'while we sleep?'

Meet Me at the Little Angel

I TRIED to persuade Ofelia sometimes that there was no work to be done, and that she might just as well go out and play. But she received the idea as though it was the whispering of the Devil. So to escape from her fury of cleaning I would go to the Reforma, with instructions for her to find me, when she had finished, at the third statue down from the little angel.

In Mexico you always give directions by the statues. You say to your driver, 'Let me off at the green Indians'; or, 'Let me off at the lions'; or, 'Let me off at the little horse.' (This is a big equestrian statue of Charles IV. Mexico does not like to remember the Spanish kings, but the little horse is so good that it has been kept 'only as a work of art,' as one reads on the base.) The city abounds

in statues, and you may be sure that the good ones date
from the colonial period, and that the bad ones are from
the time of Porfirio Díaz, when all the sweet kindly im-
pulses that did not find expression in government found
their expression in statuary.

I felt it was my civic duty to look at all the statues on
the Reforma and find out who they were. So one day I
started my inspection, but gave it up to watch a charro
on horseback courting a nursemaid. She walked alongside
the horse, wheeling the baby carriage, while he held the
baby on his arm, very proud and paternal, and the horse
stepped carefully with a high gentle prance. And it was
lovely to watch them moving under the trees, in the shade
and in the sun that gleamed on his wide sombrero. In
Europe there may be more impressive boulevards than the
Reforma, but none with its charm of informality. You sit
in the shade and watch the charros at their courting, and
the burros come ambling over the lawns and crop the grass
around the statues, and a cargador passes with a huge
easy-chair or bed-spring that some señora has ordered in
the market, and the campesinos come in from the country
— whole committees of them in to see so-and-so about
their lands and water. It is a marvelous pageant, relaxing
to the spirit; and especially so for Americans, who come
from a country where there is nothing drearier than sitting
on a park bench.

And the same informality holds for all the city. Juan
de Letran is a wide avenue, pride of the Chamber of Commerce, but the peddlers have taken possession of it and
one can buy anything there from a fountain pen to a
coyote. And on Bolívar, which is a busy cross-street, the

Indians sit on the curb knitting socks, and the acrobats perform right in the midst of the traffic. But the pitchmen favor the streets around the Plaza. They have megaphones and they collect a crowd with the loud announcement: 'Now begins the propaganda.' (It is usually about Palmolive soap.) Even Government buildings have no starched front. The National Palace corresponds to our White House, and you may catch a glimpse of el presidente there. But the campesinos squat in front of it and heat their tortillas on little carbon stoves, and anyone may enter, though two soldiers guard the gates with gleaming bare bayonets.

Naturally, the Chamber of Commerce is very much against all this, and the papers are filled with their impassioned appeals. 'How long, how long,' they cry in effect, 'will our fair city remain a village and a market-place?' They want to do away with the peddlers, the beggars and the strolling performers — in short, with all the gaiety and sadness of the streets. And instead they want order, order and cleanliness and quiet to impress the visiting Americans. There was a great campaign for cleanliness, but it seems to have miscarried like so many things in Mexico, and the newspaper bore the sad notice: 'The city celebrates Cleanliness Week and the streets remain dirtier than ever.' There was another campaign against noise on which one paper made the sorrowful comment: 'The campaign against noise steals in quietly.' The future, of course, is with the Chamber of Commerce, but that future is a long way off, and the trouble is deeper than they realize.

Because Mexico City is not made of one piece like our

own cities. An American city may be an ugly hodge-podge. It may have its slums close to rich sections, and its unemployed idle in the shade of busy factories. But all its contradictions are part of one age, part of its industrial growth. But Mexico City is different. For all the shining new cars that rush so wildly through the streets, and the modern hotels proudly advertising 'Stean Heat,' and the skyscrapers built on special foundations on the swampy ground, the modernism of the city is only the thinnest veneer over all its past. It is still a village, part of the primitive countryside around it and the primitive Indian life. It is still the colonial city of the Spaniards, and the romantic nineteenth-century city of Porfirio Díaz; it is only superficially of this century and the things of this century. It is like a fresco in which there is no perspective to make things recede in time and space. Everything is of the present, jumbled together. One remembers the words of Bernal Díaz del Castillo, who was one of the soldiers who followed Cortés, and who in his old age sat down to write 'the true history of the conquest,' very indignant over the lies that had been told about it. 'And so I say and affirm that everything written in this book is very true, and that as an eye-witness I found myself in all the battles and encounters of war; and they are not old tales which I tell, nor stories about the Romans of seven hundred years ago. For in a manner of speaking all that I tell happened only yesterday.' He wrote that four centuries ago, and one still feels that all that has happened in Mexico was only yesterday.

I think the markets have not changed much. When the Spaniards had come to the city, by perilous marches over the mountains from the seacoast, and after they had met Montezuma with great ceremony and received lodgings in the palace, they sallied forth like good tourists to see the market. And it must have been very much like those that tourists see today.

'And when we had come to the Grand Plaza, as we had never beheld such a thing, we were astonished at the multitude of people and the abundance of merchandise, and the order and arrangement that there was in everything. And I will mention first the vendors of gold and silver and precious stones, and feathers and robes and embroidered things.[1] Then there were other vendors who sold cloth and ropes of hennequen, and sandals, which are the shoes that they wear, and everything was in one part of the Plaza in its appropriate place. Let us go and talk of those who sold beans and herbs and other vegetables. Let us go to those who sold chickens and rabbits and hares and other things of the sort. Let us speak of those who sold pottery made in a thousand different ways from big basins to little pitchers, which were by themselves apart, and also of those who sold honey and sweetmeats, and wood and firewood and resinous pine strips.'

The list gets so long that he adds rather testily: 'What more do you want me to say?' Naturally he could not mention the ugly lithograph calendars (made in Japan) which are now sold in the markets and which Mexicans buy for their gorgeous color, though they may be unable to read the days of the month; or the glittering pins with false stones (made in the United States), which Mexicans

---

[1] All these things, however, have since moved into the tourist stores, where they command a better price.

prefer to their own silverwork. The resinous pine strips that he mentions are still used for a quick fuel; and because they are so much used, together with charcoal, the land around Mexico City has been denuded of its forests. But now the Government is talking of using its newly recovered oil for making gas, which is still a luxury in Mexico. And the little pitchers that were by themselves apart, are still the chief kitchenware. They are made of mud and sell for a centavo. One need stand on the streets only three minutes to see a cargador pass with a huge pile of them on his back.

But the Spaniards seem to have suffered the usual tourist difficulties, for, as Bernal Díaz says, 'the Plaza was so big and full of people it was impossible to see everything in one day.' And so they left the market and went to see the great temple, ascending the hundred and fourteen steps with the aid of two priests, whom Montezuma sent to help them so that they should not get tired.

'And as we climbed to the top of the grand temple, we came to a platform covered with stones, where they placed the sad Indians for sacrifice. And there was a dragon-like figure and other evil figures, and much blood that had been spilt that day. And as we reached it the great Montezuma came out from the place where he had been praying, where his accursed idols were, and this was high up on the temple. And with the great respect that he showed to Cortés and to all of us, he said: "Tired you must be, Señor Malinche, from your great climb." And Cortés told him through our interpreters that neither he nor any of us ever tired in anything.' (An ideal quality for tourists.)

Then Montezuma took Cortés by the hand and told him

to look at the great city and all its environs, and it was very easy to see everything 'because that accursed temple lorded it over everything.' And they saw the three great highways leading into the city, and all the canals and the great lake of Texcoco crowded with canoes coming and going. The highways are still the same, but few of the canals are left now, and those near the city are muddied with pestilential drainage waters. And the great lake of Texcoco is dry, a tiny Sahara from which dense yellow clouds of dust rise in the rainy season to envelop the city. And all the glory of Tenochtitlan, the city that Cortés gazed on from the temple, is gone too. It withstood the siege of the Spaniards and their Indian allies for sixty-five days — a siege by land and water, for Cortés ordered ships built and launched them on the lake, and from them discharged the big guns on the city. And whatever the fighting did not destroy, the Spaniards destroyed when they entered the city again. But at first they could not stay there because of the mountains of corpses and the stench from them. They withdrew to near-by Coyoacan, place of the coyote.

The great Indian city is gone, but the sad Indians remain. One is curious to know whether Bernal Díaz found all the Indians sad, or only those who were about to be sacrificed, in which case it is very understandable. But it is certain that the Indians of today are sad. It may be racial, or it may be a sadness that comes from the conditions of their life. In the four centuries following the conquest nothing was added to the life of the Indians, everything was taken away. The Indians lived, and still live, under the most primitive conditions — a degraded form of the primitive because it is not a cultural stage, but a total deprivation of all that human beings should have. Only since the Revolution have the Indians been counted as part of the population of Mexico, and they are, whether pure-blooded or mixed, a good three fifths of it. But the work of the Revolution can better their lives only slowly, but that is its chief task, and it is the future of Mexico. The sad Indians had the first word, and they will probably have the last.

And they come to the city as though it were only a big village, and they never take the streets seriously, but sit down to rest or eat their tortillas in front of the modern buildings. Groups of campesinos come in their white smocks and white trousers, sandaled or barefoot, with leather bags slung over their shoulders, on pilgrimage to the Virgin of Guadalupe or to see about their lands. And they gape up at the big buildings, or look into the store windows where there are displays of modern farm machinery, or stand listening to a gramophone bawling American jazz. I think it is this constant reminder of the primitive in a modern setting that gives Mexico its quality of excitement. And it makes for comedy too.

I remember one day in the Alameda. It is a park in the center of town, bosky and well-treed like all the parks of the city, but cluttered with bad statues. At the end near the Palace of Fine Arts, the Inquisition used to burn its victims. Later it became a fashionable promenade. Now it is a pleasant place to read the paper, to have your shoes shined, to pass the siesta hours while you wait for the city to come to life again. I was reading the paper near one of the statues — a whipped-cream female nude — when the

sound of suppressed laughter made me look up. A man
and a woman, barefoot and very ragged (they may have
been Otomís to judge by their speech), were looking at the
statue, nudging each other, laughing with their hands to
their mouths, finding it indescribably funny. It was the
most forthright piece of art criticism I have ever seen, and
I enjoyed that statue with them, as I have enjoyed few
works of art. Later a campesino came to have his picture
taken. There are photographers in the Alameda who give
you a donkey to sit on, or a sarape to drape over your
shoulder, or a big oleograph of the Cathedral of Guadalupe for a background. This photographer happened to
have a huge bull fiddle, and the campesino posed himself
with it, and everyone stopped to watch in utter solemnity.
Only the gringa laughed and went off in disgrace, but with
a feeling that the day had been well spent.

That was the day I bought a parrot for Ofelia. I thought
she might keep it in the hut, and it would distract her
from the housecleaning, and I would have more time alone.

'He is well behaved, señora,' the old man said when he
sold it to me. 'He is not vulgar. He will never embarrass
you.' The parrot eyed me slyly and malevolently, like a
wrongdoer who hears his lawyer praising him in court.
'He is a Christian, señora. His name is Leopoldo, and he
has very good antecedents.'

I took the Christian Leopoldo home, and Ofelia took
him to her house, and for a time it was very easy to persuade her not to work, on the grounds that Leopoldo
needed her care. He did behave very well at the beginning,
but it turned out that he was only biding his time. Ofelia
came up one day very alarmed.

'Señora, I believe we will have to get rid of the parrot. Forgive us, señora, but we cannot keep him, not another day, my father says.'

'But why, Ofelia?'

'Pues, as we are so many in the hut . . .'

'But you could put him outside.'

She broke down completely. 'Ay, señora, the things he said! They were not to be listened to by decent people. If you had heard him, señora!'

I was really sorry that Leopoldo was not the Christian we had thought him to be, for it was a time of great peace for me. But there was nothing to be done about it, and Ofelia sold him to the man who came to grind the knives, and recommended him as a model of behavior.

To Eat with Confidence

'WELL, he is coming,' Ofelia said one day.

'Who?'

'Why, Daniel.' She had a way of continuing conversations that had long since passed from my memory. 'Already he has reached Guadalajara, where he ordered a letter sent to us. He came there from my pueblo on a burro, for the cheapness of it, with his sweetheart and a basket of chicks which we will raise for their eggs. Now, with the train from Guadalajara he will be here in no time.'

She polished the knife she was drying, and sighed: 'The question of a wedding dress preoccupies me.'

But I did not answer at once, thinking of Daniel and his sweetheart. I saw them riding the burro, the girl in back of Daniel with her arms around his waist, and Daniel very busy hitting the burro with his legs. And then they were in Guadalajara, where they stood a long time in admiration of the Cathedral, and then they sought out a scribe in the market-place to write the letter. Daniel dictated it and watched the mysterious words forming; but the girl was bored and lifted the lid of the basket and looked at the chicks.

'Do you think you would like a dress of pink silk?' I asked Ofelia.

'I am very fond of pink silk,' she said, with just the right touch of reserve. But then she added firmly: 'It is not urgent, however. My father says Daniel must find work before he may marry. Perhaps the boss will make him a watchman of the new building.'

The scribe must have delayed sending the letter; for Daniel came the next morning, right on the heels of it, so to speak. I saw him outside the hut. His sweetheart was washing his hair, and all the Escotos were standing around in a state of great hilarity. He had brought many foods with him from Atotonilco, and Ofelia said I was to come in the evening, first to acquaint myself with these foods, and then to meet Daniel. So all day I avoided passing the hut, so that my presentation to Daniel might be formal as they wished it to be; and I waited until well after dark before knocking at the door. Mexicans do not rush the day off unceremoniously as we do. It is still 'Good afternoon' at eight o'clock, or even nine o'clock — as long, in fact, as there is the faintest glimmer of light in the sky.

Mrs. Escoto introduced me simply as 'the señora,' and Daniel and his girl smiled politely and made room for me on the bed. Daniel was built small and slender as a jockey. He looked like all the Escoto children — green eyes and sandy hair, a güero or blond. But he had buck teeth, and my first thought was that he did not look as bright as the others. His sweetheart was a strapping girl, dark and boyish, with high cheekbones and a fine smile. I kept looking and looking at her, to conclude in the end that she was thoroughly fascinating.

'Ay, señora,' Mrs. Escoto said, and blew away the formalities with her sigh. 'Ofelia bothered me so all afternoon! "That you do not make tortillas, for the señora does not eat them." "That you do not make frijoles, for the señora does not like them." Following me around and talking and talking until I was nearly crazy, and could not concentrate properly on the cooking. So that if the dishes should not please you...'

'Vaya!' I said, 'how will they not please me, when I have long awaited this opportunity to savor the true Mexican cooking.'

'Ah, really, señora? Then how relieved I am. You are not afraid to eat with us? Then how relieved I am.' She smiled broadly and sat down, taking her place with the women against the wall. They sat on boxes in a row, crouching, holding the long ends of their rebozos between their arms — the old grandmother, who kept looking from one to another with her bright unseeing birdlike eyes, and Mrs. Escoto and the two aunts. The younger aunt, she whose husband had left her, was very pretty. She sat modestly and with downcast eyes. But the older one, who had the sickness of which they knew so little, not even the name, was sharp-featured and bright-eyed with suffering.

It was she who always greeted me with 'How did the dawn find you?' — the melancholy greeting of an invalid, for whom each dawn must be a stock-taking of pains. There was only candlelight in the room, and the women sitting in shadow and sheathed in their long rebozos looked like sculpture, like the repeated figures on a frieze.

Daniel had been giving them the news of their tierra when I came in, and now, with many apologies to me, he continued — telling them of deaths and marriages, of births and sicknesses, of so-and-so who had grown paralyzed, of another who had committed a murder and fled to the mountains. And they listened gravely and without comment, as people do who receive news rarely, and who know that from the things that happen in life there is no appeal. The room was crowded, for now with Daniel and his girl there were fourteen to live in the hut; and as I listened I wondered about their lives, about their intimacies and sexuality. But the real wonder was how, from this herdlike, comfortless, and starving life of theirs, came such dignity, such graciousness and chaste reserve.

Daniel spoke for a long time, but at last silence fell on his narrative, and Mrs. Escoto rose, sighing over all she had heard, and went into the other room where the foods were cooking on an open fire. She came back bearing a packing-case which she set before me, and over it she laid a white cloth. 'Then you are really not afraid to eat with us?' she asked again, and again I assured her that I was not.

Señor Escoto encouraged me. 'This of eating strange foods,' he mused, 'it is something one must venture boldly and with confidence.' He stood leaning against the door, looking out on the street and the quiet blue night, as if he had some need to show he was not quite part of this womanish gathering.

'As we should do, señora,' said the younger aunt, 'if ever it should be our good fortune to visit over there in your country.' She offered cigarettes, the small thin ones that are bought at five for a centavo, and then the candle was passed around to light them. But Señor Escoto waved it away and used a gold cigarette lighter for his. Only he seemed to want to hide it, and he put it away quickly. 'And is the tortilla consumed much over there, señora?'

'Little. It is a delicacy over there.'

'Really? Then what do they eat over there?' The tone of her voice clearly implied that obviously, in that case, we do not eat at all.

Mrs. Escoto came in with the first of the dishes, Ofelia and her little sisters following in procession. There was corn baked on the cob, a great delicacy in Mexico where most of the corn is used for making tortillas; and there were tortillas — the thin flabby ones which must be eaten hot or they taste like seaweed, and the thick crisp ones mixed with flour, which are much more like our idea of a biscuit. And there was a soup of corn, with meat and sharp green chiles; and atole, mentioned by the chroniclers as the beverage of Montezuma, lord of the Aztecs. It is a gruel of corn and chocolate. They whirl a stick in it, much as though they were making fire, and the gruel gets frothy and foamy. And there was also purslane fried in lard and a dish of the spiny cactus leaves of the nopal. But these greens were only condiments for the dishes of corn, which is consumed in so many ways in Mexico that the different forms of it seem like the varying manifestations of the corn goddess.

Mrs. Escoto arrayed everything before me, and then she sat down well pleased. 'Know, señora, that here is your home and here we are at your service. Whenever you have the whim to taste what is typically Mexican — something they have told you about or that you have tasted in the restaurants ...'

'Vaya!' Señor Escoto took his glance from the street to rebuke her. 'And if she prefers the restaurants?'

The smell of corn filled the room, and I was hungry and wondered when they would eat. But nobody moved to the table and there was a silence, while Mrs. Escoto made a pleased purring sound in her throat, a sort of wordless speech binding us all together in comradely well-being. Smoke came in from the other room. 'Ay, the calabash!' she cried, and jumped up and ran inside. Ofelia followed, and her voice drifted back in a whisper meant for secrecy, but loud enough to be heard. *But she eats with the knife and the fork, I tell you.*

'Pues, señora' — the young aunt cast her eyes down modestly — 'that is something we have never learned. The knife and the fork.'

'As it is not needed in our diet ...' said the older aunt, and I heard myself roundly denouncing the knife and the fork. It was merely the custom of my country, a custom for barbarous meat-eaters. 'Ah, yes, the question of customs,' Señor Escoto mused wisely, and then Mrs. Escoto came back with the calabash and a small earthenware pitcher which she thrust into Daniel's hands.

'You will go for pulque.'

My heart sank, for I had heard the sturdiest travelers describe pulque with horror — the white yeasty-looking drink made from the juice of the maguey plant, into which all kinds of ordure is put to make it ferment more rapidly. It may be pure and palatable when drunk in the country on the hacienda where it is made. But pulque of the city that is sold for six centavos a pitcher in the paper-beribboned pulquerías is not recommended for the palate or for the nostrils. The legend is that an Indian princess, Xochitl, discovered how to make pulque, and some authorities say that the Indians before the time of the conquest never took it to excess. But today, in a land where water is scarce and where the diet gives no sustenance, pulque is both water and nourishment, a giver of energy for a while and ultimately of death, for it is a perfect culture for many different kinds of disease-bearing bacteria.

Daniel was already at the door when I protested. 'So much trouble for him. Please do not bother. Really I had not expected pulque and I shall not be the least disappointed not to have it.'

'Pues . . .' Mrs. Escoto hesitated. 'Know, señora, that we ourselves do not drink it, but it is very typical.'

'Yes, typical!' the young aunt said scornfully. 'But it is the great vice of our Mexicans, and one is better off without it.'

'A vice, nothing less.' Señor Escoto spoke with unwonted energy. 'Know that in our tierra it is not much consumed. We of Jalisco are not like those of the mesa here, drunk and besodden with pulque-drinking. I myself have never touched it, nor would I permit the drinking of it here in this house.'

I was not sure, but I thought he looked meaningly at Daniel, who stood at the door looking from one to another and grinning broadly, as if this discussion amused him inordinately.

'Then that I do not violate the customs of this house,' I said fervently, and Daniel sat down again, still very much amused.

Señor Escoto bestirred himself in answer to signals from his wife. 'Well, there is some tequila,' he said with a touch of reluctance, and produced a bottle from behind the packing-case that served as altar for the Virgin. 'This is permitted, yes. We do not have it often, señora, but it is a gift from my compadre there in Guadalajara.'

'And do you know Guadalajara?' Daniel asked politely, while his father poured the tequila.

'No, I do not. And I am very much ashamed that I do not know Guadalajara.'

'Then you must make its acquaintance. It is a wonderful city,' said Daniel, who had been there a few hours.

'Guadalajara!' Mrs. Escoto looked at him scornfully, shifting her rebozo. 'What would the señora find there to amuse her? The señora comes from New York. Now that, I believe, is a city.'

'Is it near the city of Michigan?' Daniel's sweetheart asked.

'No, it is not near Michigan, which is not a city either, but a state.'

'That is sad, then. Because the husband of a girl in our tierra went to the United States and got lost in Michigan. And she weeps weeps weeps for him all the time.'

'How silly,' Ofelia said. 'If he were my husband I should go to Michigan and find him.'

'And you would lose yourself too,' her father chided her. He lit another cigarette, furtively as before, with the gold cigarette lighter. 'Many of our Mexicans lose themselves in the United States. Your country has a great fascination for us, señora.'

'Not more than Mexico for us, señor,' I countered politely. 'We come now by the thousands to enjoy the beauties of your country.'

'Yes, the boss was telling me the city is full of Americans. Mucho turista, mucho turista!' he said. For the Mexican, to describe the presence of large numbers of any plague like flies or tourists or insects, will say: much fly, much tourist, much insect. 'The boss hopes they will come and live in the houses, which he is having built to the specifications of an American who claims that he knows what your countrymen like. True that they are houses pleasing to you Americans?'

'True,' I said, thinking of the bathtub that drained the wrong way, the shower that hit the wall, and other details of the splendid but misguided plumbing which Mexicans install in their houses with great enthusiasm and a total lack of workability.

'Yes, yes, much tourist,' he nodded, drawing on his cigarette. 'They travel all over the country.'

'Nor do they have to pay,' said Mrs. Escoto, 'which makes it exceedingly easy.'

'But certainly we must pay!' I exclaimed.

'Ah — then you do not travel free? Then I do not understand it. How you can travel around so much if you must pay!'

'It is because one dollar is worth many pesos.'

'I do not understand that either.'

'Nor I,' I said frankly, never having understood the mysteries of foreign exchange. 'But look you. If I have an American dollar, I can go to a money-changer on Isabela la Católica and get five pesos for it.'

'That is very convenient.'

'I have found it so.'

She sighed. 'If only we all had dollars, for then we could go back to our tierra. But look you, señora, it is a great outlay and there are many of us. It would be a fortune. So that it is likely we shall never see our tierra again, for lack of the money to go there.'

'Nor is there necessity,' Señor Escoto told her brusquely. 'We are well enough here. And now that Daniel has come...'

Daniel clasped his knees, leaned back and smiled while everyone looked at him. 'But my fancy,' he said with a worldly air, 'is to travel. I would like to visit your tierra, señora. Already I know several English words, which an American taught me on the train.'

'Ay, Daniel, what a scholar you are!' his sweetheart teased.

'His mouth was always too much open,' Ofelia said. 'Flies got in, and now, it seems, English words.'

'For shame, Ofelia, to talk so of your brother.' Mrs. Escoto turned to me. 'No, señora, Daniel is really bright. He always had a gift for learning. But this Ofelia here has a great deal of malice in her. She is very presuming and I cannot imagine what sort of a woman she will be. Already the men look at her. It is something in her blood, I believe. I do not know what she has in her blood, that already the men look at her, with her braids still down her back.'

Ofelia blushed, while her mother continued sternly: 'And do you remember in the train from Guadalajara? Far from putting yourself out to learn anything, you smiled at the trainman. He made a pet of her and bought her candy and tweaked her braids. Truly it was scandalous. So that I am afraid here in the city to let her walk far from the house. And the only way I know that she has gone to the doctrine on Tuesdays is by asking her what is new in the catechism. You see, señora, we in Mexico are somewhat wild. And it is nothing for a man to take a girl by her braids and drag her away and do her a grave injury.'

'Yes, we are savages,' Señor Escoto said, rather satisfied.

'And over there' — the young aunt looked down modestly — 'it is very different, isn't it ...' But Daniel spared me the problem of answering.

'How I should like to visit over there! Tell me, señora, do they speak Spanish at all over there?'

'That you do not speak stupidities!' his father eyed him sternly. 'Clearly they do not speak Spanish over there, for look you, they come here and they cannot even speak it.'

'Yes, it is a barbarity, this speech of the tourists,' Daniel agreed. 'Already I have heard two of them asking the way to a certain street, and it was a strange way they spoke, very far from our Castilian. Almost they sounded like the little Indians who come trotting in from the mountains with their carbon and wood for sale. God knows what idiom these Indians speak, but we' — his glance swept everyone present, while his gesture took in all those of his tierra — 'we speak Spanish!'

But his pride and scorn fell on a silence, for of a sudden we were all staring at the table. By now it was late enough even for Mexicans to consider it supper-time, and I felt very hungry. But the food remained untouched like a still-life on the table, though it was a banquet such as they had probably not tasted in years.

Ofelia came timidly from her corner. 'Well, it is as I thought,' she said sadly. 'She does not like our food.'

'Nonsense, child. I have not even tasted it.'

'Because you do not like it, señora. Obviously!'

'No, I am waiting until everyone eats, nothing more.'

'Ah, she is waiting until everyone eats, nothing more,' the young aunt echoed softly, explaining to everyone.

'Pues...' Mrs. Escoto arose majestically, and her long-toothed smile was triumphant. 'It has all been a mis-understanding. For just imagine, señora, here we have been sitting and thinking that you disdained our foods.'

'But on the contrary!'

'Then eat, eat!' she said imperiousiy, and shoved the plates toward me. 'Ourselves, we have eaten to satiety today. It is all for you.'

'Ah, then it is all too much.'

'Ah, then you really do not like it.'

'Obviously,' the old aunt said accusingly, and everyone agreed: Obviously!

'No, no. Only I shall feel so greedy dining alone.'

'Would to Allah,' Señor Escoto concluded the argument fervently. 'Would to Allah that you feel greedy! For then we shall no longer experience doubts.'

So I fell to, thinking that here was the ultimate refinement of courtesy — not to eat with one's guest, but to cause him to eat alone in solitary state. But, like all refinements, there was cruelty in it. I felt like the trapped bird who is fed strange foods while his captors look on. And something of my terror must have shown in my face, for Mrs. Escoto said: 'Eat, señora, eat with confidence.'

But while I ate with confidence there came a knock at the door. 'Ave María,' a voice said.

And everyone in the room responded, 'De gracia.'

It was the first of the guests come to see Daniel, and after that many more came.

6

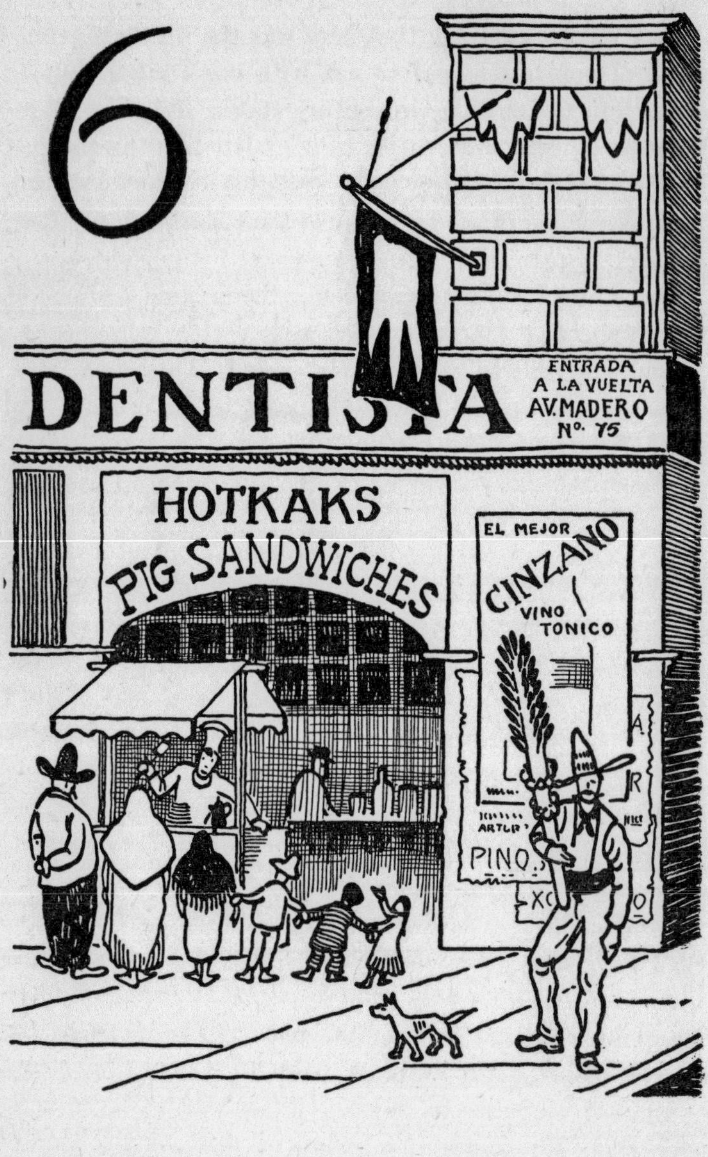
DENTISTA
ENTRADA
A LA VUELTA
AV. MADERO
Nº. 75
HOTKAKS
PIG SANDWICHES
EL MEJOR
CINZANO
VINO
TONICO

'Allo Good-bye

DANIEL wanted to continue the study of English that he had begun on the train, and so he would knock at my door, and when I opened he would stand there smiling and embarrassed, shifting his posture many times before he spoke. 'Señora,' he would ask finally, 'could you give me some English words?' It was like a neighbor coming to borrow salt.

On the train he had learned to say ''allo, good-bye,' and 'Worldes Fair'! (This last with a great deal of conviction.) So I gave him a few more such words each time, and he learned them diligently, and I felt that very soon the Escotos could put out a sign such as one sees on the tourist stores in the center of town: ENGLISH IS SPOKEN.

English is spoken in Mexico City, to which there is no objection. But in addition Spanish is absorbing a flood of undigested English words, which may make for a very sad jargon of the two languages in the future. On the sports pages of the newspapers you read about 'beisbol' and 'boxeo,' 'el noqueout' and 'el upper-cut.' The society pages announce: 'Gran preview en un night club,' and invite you to 'bailar swing'; and in the news you read of a political 'mitin' that was addressed by 'un líder.' You may have your shoes shined by a 'chainero' (so called because he gives you a 'chain'), and you may stop at a 'Lonchería' and order 'hotkaks' and 'pig sandwichs.' The stores sell three pieces of furniture as 'un set,' and a funny picture is 'un derroche de laughs.' I felt that the coming of the New York Follies boded no good for Mexico, and my fears were confirmed when a huge sign appeared on the Palace of Fine Arts: 'LAS GLAMOUR GIRLS Y LAS LOVELIES DEBUTAN HOY.'

This influx of English words worries many Mexicans, especially those who have the dignity of their language at heart. Latin-Americans have an attitude toward their language which it is hard for us to understand. They are very proud of it, very jealous of it, as they are proud and jealous of all their culture, while we Americans are more concerned about our comfort and material well-being. It is an attitude that comes to them from the Spaniards, who alone among all the nations of western Europe did not develop along material lines, but remained an otherworldly people, given to philosophy and introspection. The Spaniards have always been very emotional about their language. They have been too emotional about it, if you wish; but still they have cherished it in the way that other nations will cherish their road mileage or their favorable balance of trade. And the Latin-Americans have inherited this attitude, and with them it has an additional emphasis. Now that the revolt against Spain is more than a century old, and all the rancors and animosities that went with it quite out of their systems, they have begun to look back to Spain again, and to re-evaluate their Spanish heritage. And in this process they find that the language is an affirming force. It binds them to all the traditions that they wish to conserve of the mother country, it is the vessel of transmission and therefore dear to them.

So the professors are busy trying to keep their language Spanish, and to find equivalents for English words. But not always with complete success. Instead of 'el sandwich,' for instance, the word 'emparedado' has been adopted. This means 'something between walls,' and though it sounds more Spanish it seems less edible. Along with 'el sandwich' there is the problem of what to call a person from the United States. In justice we should not be called 'Americanos,' for all the people of the western world are Americans, and there is no reason why we should monopolize the term. To the nations south of us we are 'los Norte-Americanos,' and that is what we are often called. But this again is unsatisfactory, because it does not distinguish us from the Canadians and the Esquimos. In strict logic, such a person should be called an 'Estadounidense.' But one much prefers the uncomplimentary 'gringo,' or the universally used 'Yanqui.'

One favors this effort to find Spanish equivalents for our words, but the future is problematical. The cultures of the United States and the Spanish-speaking world are at present at different levels. Neither Spain nor the countries of Latin-America are industrialized nations, and for that reason Spanish lacks many words for things, machines, processes that already exist in English. Our exports and our general influence are bound to bring them these lacking words — and in our language. And this process will coincide with a period in which the Latin-American masses grow more literate, with more books, newspapers, and magazines in circulation, all of which will act as agents to spread our words.

Or will they do just the opposite, and educate our neighbors to more and better Spanish? It is very dangerous to make prophecies, and perhaps one should say only that the fight between English and Spanish will be on in earnest, with forces aiding both languages. Thus far, it is certain, Spanish has shown itself very stubborn. In the four centuries during which it has lived in the new world in contact with many different Indian tongues, it has resisted change, remained essentially itself. Of course Spanish was the superior language and belonged to the superior culture, and that may account for its staying intact. But how if our neighbors to the south feel that it is also superior to English, and the culture of things and machinery that English represents? They call the words that we have given to their language 'barbarismos'; which reminds one uncomfortably that they sometimes call us, too, barbarians — the barbarians in the North.

And Spanish has survived with a great deal of uniformity throughout the nations that speak it in this hemisphere. National differences of speech do exist, but no person from one Latin-American country has difficulty in understanding a person from another. And what is more surprising, in understanding a Spaniard from Europe. The language has changed, naturally, on both sides of the ocean since the time that Spanish was extended to the new world, but the changes on our side have closely paralleled those that have occurred in Spain, because they have been the natural changes within the laws of philology.

So we are told by the philologists, who happen to have very little influence on the human instinct for snobbery. Like the Englishman who comes to the United States, the Spaniard from the peninsula often comes to Latin-America with the feeling that there they must speak a quite inferior brand of his language. If he is a Castilian, he is especially proud of his theta, the lisping 'th' sound where most Latin-Americans use an 's' sound. The Spaniard from Europe is very apt to feel that the language in the new world has declined sadly since the time of the conquerors. But to take the conquerors as models of linguistic perfection is pure fantasy, on a par with some of our ideas about our first settlers. There were among the conquerors some of more or less fame who could not even read or write, and all the conquerors were rough-and-ready adventurers. And they had scant respect for the Indian names of places. Many of the Mexican place-names that sound to us so purely Indian are only what the Spaniards thought they heard the Indians say. They managed to get some very queer versions of the names they heard, in which, perhaps, they were not unlike the tourists of our day.

I resisted all the efforts of my Spanish friends to make me talk with the theta, for I wanted my Spanish to have the stamp of the country where I had learned it. But I did not feel that I spoke like a real Mexican until I could use the diminutive with the recklessness with which the Mexicans use it. One feels sometimes that one is in a world of midgets, to hear a Mexican talk of 'his little mother,' 'his little grandmother,' 'his little friend.' Or that everything on the market has shrunk to miniature size: 'Buy, buy, señorita! A little purse — a little broom.' Or that everything is exquisitely dainty: 'I put on my little blouse and my little skirt, my little shoes —' The news-vendor, giving you change, asks: 'Have you a little penny?' And the waitress brings you the little check and you leave her the little tip. And then there is 'ahorita,' which means 'in a little right away,' and which puts you off very gracefully. And there is 'tantito,' over which I have brooded for hours. 'How can you eat tantito?' — 'so much of a little bit'?

It is said that this prodigal use of the diminutive ending comes from a form in the Nahuatl language, which was spoken by the Aztecs and is still spoken in Mexico today. But I think there is more in it than that. For so many centuries the Mexican peon lived in a state of serfdom, entirely dependent on the lord of the hacienda for everything he needed. And when he asked for anything it had to be done with servile humility, he could not ask but had to beg. What more natural than that he should minimize what he was asking for, as today the beggars ask for 'una socorrita, por dios!' — 'a little piece of charity'? And I think it is also a form of delicacy in speech, part of that marvelous courtesy which one observes in all classes, and in the people of the streets more than in others.

I wanted to acquire a reasonable amount of slang, too,

but it hasn't much vogue in Mexico. Speech is very much
of one piece among all classes, though naturally there are
words that belong to various trades, not all respectable.
But slang is not created with such speed and variety as
among the Americans, probably because city life is not so
developed. I remember a night at El Chino's, when I
boasted of the superior vividness of the American language, and the affronted Mexicans challenged me to prove
it, and we began making lists on the paper napkins. I
could muster more slang, but they won in poetic expressions, with some really splendid proverbs and comparisons
based on the age-old simplicities of country life. Nor does
Spanish lend itself to slang. It is not fast enough. Take
our retort, 'Horse feathers!' In Spanish you would have
to say, 'las plumas de un caballo' — 'the feathers of a
horse' — which sounds like a mistake on the menu. One
notes the difference at the movies, in the way English
dialogue is translated into Spanish subtitles. 'Skip it!'
becomes 'let us leave that topic.' 'He's up against it,'
turns into 'he finds himself in difficulties.' And a beauty
like, 'Listen, sister, dames like you can't afford to be too
choosy,' is just left severely alone.

I went to the movies to learn the colloquial expressions,
but it did not help much, and I found that when slang
did appear I resented it because it did not seem to me to
ring true. That was because, as the grammars recommend,
I had begun to think in Spanish — which means to think
in very dignified phrases. Soon I could think with as much
dignity as Ofelia, and it no longer struck me as funny
when she used an expression that English reserves for
learned professors. I did not see her on the morning

after Daniel's arrival, but she came up later full of apologies.

'Ay, señora,' she sighed, 'forgive me, but I am so disoriented. All night we have been listening to that Daniel with his stories, and it has been so diverting...'

Sí, No Hay

DANIEL found work as a night watchman on one of the buildings, and in the early hours his sweetheart came and kept him company. Señor Escoto also stood guard at night, but nearer to the house; and whenever I passed late I would see him standing in the shadows, immobile, holding his sarape across his face for fear of the night air. It needed the 'buenas noches' that we exchanged to assure me that it was he. For the Mexican changes in the dark, becomes part of the night and the shadows. I liked walking late on the deserted streets, when the white-walled buildings seemed still as ruins in the moonlight, and only the wandering watchman was abroad, playing musically on his whistle. Sometimes I saw him, a ghostly figure wrapped in his sarape as in a medieval cloak, haunting the streets with silent footfall. His whistle must have warned thieves and wrongdoers of his whereabouts, and I imagine that they listened for the sound of it and then went quietly to where he was not. But probably it was not meant to frighten them, but only to assure the good citizens in their beds that all was well. The watchmen used to carry torches and call 'Ave María Purísima.' One cannot hear that call any more, but the torches can still be bought in the Thieves' Market.

And walking through the streets at night I used to think of the city's legends, the weird and fearful legends that do not seem things of the past in the city's strange atmosphere. There was La Llorona, the weeping one, who wailed through the streets at night, punished because she had betrayed her people to the conquerors; and La Mulata, the witch who flew through prison bars to escape the torture of the Inquisition; and a host of others, demons and witches and ghosts and assassins. It is a city twice haunted, from the time when it was Tenochtitlan of the Aztecs, and from the time of the friars, who brought the middle ages to Mexico and all their demonology and superstition.

But the legend I liked best concerns a nobleman whose name I have forgotten. The story is that he burst from his house one night and ran insanely through the streets, asking of all whom he met: 'Do you know the day of your death?' And those who answered no, he killed, saying: 'Unfortunate one, that you did not know the day of your death.' And those who answered yes, he also killed, with a 'Fortunate one, that you knew the day of your death.' It was this nobleman with his poor sense of humor whom

I should least have wanted to meet when I walked alone at night. How much pleasanter to meet Daniel and his girl, and to hear their friendly 'buenas noches' from the shadow of the building where he kept guard.

Things were better now that Daniel had come. The chickens grew and soon Ofelia was selling their eggs. 'You see,' she said proudly, 'now we have more money. My father says there will soon be enough to buy me shoes.' I was not very enthusiastic about buying the eggs, for the chickens gorged on all the refuse on the lot. The privy for all the families was on the other side of the lot, against a blank wall. I bought the eggs and put them away and used the tiny brown ones that Manolo sold so expensively in the store. Yet this was pure self-deception, and soon I gave up worrying about the matter at all. The practical side of life in Mexico is difficult enough, and if one is to worry about all the precautions against disease there is little time left for anything else. Water must be boiled, milk must be boiled, and vegetables are a problem. The Indians who bring them in from the outlying districts dip them in the filthy waters of the drainage canals, 'so that they may not turn sad,' as Ofelia put it. I told her never to buy clean vegetables, but to prefer them with the sand and grit of mother earth on them; and we washed them over and over, and lettuce was soaked with drops of iodine to guard against dysentery.

I hold no brief for the lack of sanitation in Mexico. But I do hold one against those Americans who act as if it was all a conspiracy against them, and believe that the Mexicans are a healthy people who rarely get sick and seldom die. I suggest that they look at the mortality statistics, which show a death-rate for Mexico so high that few countries in the world can hope to equal it. And I suggest that they do so because the first step in understanding a people is to know the extent of their mortality, the things from which they suffer and die.

But the question of time is another story. There I stay with the Americans; for the lack of punctuality is really something to shatter the well-ordered soul. There is only one thing that ever begins on time in Mexico, and that is the bullfight. And yes, the siesta hour too. At one o'clock the storekeepers roll down the iron curtains of their shops with such zeal and haste that the unwary buyer may well be decapitated. But otherwise everything is run as if clocks had never been invented, and the time was just something you made up out of your own head. The same for the calendar. I went to the University to attend the first class of the term, and found a few professors loitering sadly in the patio.

'Where is the class of Professor Jiménez Rueda?' I asked.

The porter pointed to a room on the balcony and chanted, 'Arriba.'

'But it is dark and no one is there.'

'Yes, it is dark and no one is there.'

'But the classes have begun?'

'Certainly they have begun.' He paused. 'Nothing more than that the students have not concurred in sufficient numbers. In effect, therefore, there are no classes.'

Of course he could have told me that at once, but a Mexican's first impulse is to please you by answering yes, and then to add the devastating detail. ('Do you live with

your parents?' I asked the little boy who carried my
things in the market. 'Yes,' he said, 'only they died and
I live with my little grandmother.')

I went back to the University several weeks later, hoping
that the students had concurred in sufficient numbers.
The gates were closed and the porter stood outside. 'They
have all gone out to take the census, señorita, the students
as well as the professors.' I should have known. It was
the week of the census and all Mexico was in a state of
suspended animation. Even the heated election campaign
had been called off so that people might stay at home to
be counted instead of running out to cheer their candidates.
And every Government office was closed tight as a drum,
and every school and library was closed, and everyone who
could handle a brief case was out trying to find twenty
million Mexicans. It is not every nation that can thus
take time off to count itself.

But believing that three is a magic number, I went to
the University again. The porter looked at me this time
as though he was not sure but what he might have a
mental case on his hands. 'Pues ... it is Expropriation
Day, señorita. The commemoration of the expropriation
of our petroleum from the Northamerican enterprises.
There is a magnificent demonstration in the Plaza. Have
you seen it?' I am not sure what I burbled in reply, but
I remember his saying, 'In Mexico one learns patience.'

And what can one do against such saintly counsel but
feel very much ashamed? Besides, it is my belief that one
should learn patience in a foreign land, for I take it that
this is the true measure of travel. If one does not suffer
some frustration of the ordinary reflexes, how can one be

sure one is really traveling? Yet I confess there were two times when this lofty philosophy of travel always collapsed, and my patience quite deserted me. The milk always arrived sour, for the delivery boys ride around town on bicycles, with the milk exposed to the sun and gently churning itself into buttermilk. It seems that nothing can be done about this. And the other time was whenever I heard the Mexican storekeeper's 'No hay!' [1] — 'There isn't any.' The Mexicans are certainly not a race of shopkeepers. They open stores but take a positive delight in frustrating the customer. Ask for what you reasonably expect the store to sell, and nine times out of ten the storekeeper begins waving his right forefinger in the air like a pendulum, and shakes his head and says: 'No hay.' It's the most negative gesture in the world. That waving forefinger simply expunges what you have asked for from the face of the earth, and meanwhile he looks at you in a way that clearly implies that you should be ashamed of yourself for asking at all. And there are various refinements of it. He may say, 'Sí, no hay' — 'Yes, there isn't any.' Or, 'Ahora no hay' — '*Now* there isn't any.' This implies that it is all your fault, since you came just at the wrong time. Now if you had only come sooner, oh, just a minute or two sooner ...

But of course this will probably pass when Mexico becomes a great industrialized country, like the Colossus to the North, as the papers call us; and when storekeepers delight in the abundance on their shelves and Mexicans have money to buy the thousand and one things that now they are too poor to buy. And then there will be a radio

[1] Pronounced: No I.

in each home, and they will no longer enjoy the sad music of the cilindro. It was Ofelia who used to lure the cilindro to our street. I came home one warm evening and found all the people from the lot gathered on the corner. The men were holding the babies on their arms, and the women stood against the building, making a frieze of rebozos.

'Has something happened?' I asked Daniel's sweetheart.

She looked at me a little contemptuously. 'No, it is the music.'

And then I realized that this was a concert, and that everyone was listening to the cilindro. A small, hump-backed, dour-looking fellow was grinding it, his head show-ing above it as on a platter. And everyone was counting, for the cilindro will play you five songs for ten centavos, and not one more or less. So everyone listened and counted, and when the last song had been played there was a general stirring, and the men looked at each other until someone reluctantly drew a coin from his pocket. And after a while no one gave any more coins, and the man shifted his cilindro to his back and went off, and the people melted away, with a few calls to the children and soft 'buenas noches.'

It is a sad diversion because all hand-organs are sad, and because all Mexican songs have a mournful, down-twisting cadence. But there is always the sound of the cilindro somewhere on the old colonial streets of the poor sections of town. It may be a group of shoemakers, busily cobbling around a table in an open stall, who pay for the cilindro; or a servant standing lonely in the door of the house at night. She listens and counts the songs, and sometimes the count is wrong and it ends in an argument.

Or it may be a group of workers waiting for the trolley in the clear twilight. They sit on the curb, very still and abstracted as if they were not listening to the music at all, but when the five songs are over someone rises and pays again. Then the trolley comes and the cilindro-grinder stops in the middle of a phrase and goes off, usually with a number of songs still unplayed, which are pure profit for him.

With the new prosperity, Ofelia spent her money reck-lessly on the cilindro. She was selling many eggs and already she had a new pair of shoes, several sizes too big to allow for future expansion. But one day, while she was mopping the floor, she said:

'Well, we are going to sell the chickens.'

'Really?'

'Yes, really. We cannot keep them any more.'

'Then you have found a buyer and a good price?'

'Oh no. But Manolo says we must sell them.'

'But that's outrageous. What right has he to tell you?'

'Pues, we are selling the eggs much cheaper than his, and he says we have started competition. Now nobody buys his eggs any more.'

'And serves him right. They are too dear.'

'And so tiny, señora. Much tinier than ours.'

'They are pigeon eggs, I'm sure. I wouldn't listen to him.'

'But he came to the house last night. He was bravo, muy bravo.'

'Bravo' is many things. A spirited animal is bravo. And piquant chile sauce is bravo. And a man like Manolo is bravo. We should call him a tough customer.

'He's a gachupín,' I said.

'What?'

'Never mind. You just don't listen to him and go on selling your eggs.'

'No, we cannot, really. Because Manolo will go to the boss, and the boss will take my father off the watch. Already Manolo says that my father steals from the buildings at night. Qué barbaridad! As if my father wouldn't have to replace whatever he steals! But he doesn't steal, señora, because he doesn't believe in it. He neither steals, nor drinks pulque, nor plays rayuela. We are decent people and not shameless ones. But this Manolo does not think so. And you, señora, what do you think?'

She looked at me fearfully and I scolded her for asking. For I had never doubted that the Escotos were decent people, 'gente decente,' which is a definite class in Mexico. But one must make it known that one is of the decent people, for there are other kinds — robbers, sneak-thieves, house-breakers, who are also a definite class, and spoken of quite as if they were pursuing a legitimate profession. Ofelia had pointed out a young man on the lot, saying, quite nonchalantly: 'They say he's a sneak-thief.' Much as one might say, 'They say he is taking up dentistry.' And there are also the sin-vergüenzas, the shameless ones. To be a shameless one is to be something very definite. I don't know quite what, but it's a recognized career. I have always felt a real weakness for the shameless ones. I imagine they are good company, full of surprises.

'You go on selling the eggs,' I told Ofelia. 'I, for one, will continue to buy them. And besides, you could put some in a basket and go on the other side of the Reforma, and sell them from house to house.'

'My mother would never permit it.'

'But she lets you go to the church, which is far away too.'

'Yes, señora, but that is the church. I go straight straight, and never talk to the peons who call to me.'

'You could talk to the maids on the lawns, and ask them if their mistresses might not want nice fresh eggs.'

'Possibly,' she conceded. 'Though the maids always have their sweethearts there, and my mother would not want me to associate with them. Besides, I must now take Lupita to the church. She is growing up quite a heathen.'

'Well, then there's no remedy,' I said, washing my hands of it.

'Sí, no hay remedio,' she sighed, very relieved.

For the sooner a Mexican can reach the point of saying 'no hay remedio — there's no remedy for it' — the happier he is. And having said it with utter resignation, everything is considered settled, and there *is* no remedy for it.

But Ofelia rallied in her own defense. 'And besides, I am very busy now,' she said, vigorously swabbing the floor. 'For I am teaching the catechism to the younger children. I must go every Tuesday to read them a portion.'

I knew Ofelia's Catholic zeal, for she delighted in standing at the window and informing me about the children playing below: 'You see, señora, those up to seven years are little angels, and the others are all sinners.' (Though I confess that from a non-theological point of view I could not always tell the difference.) But I had never known that she could read.

'Pues, I really do not,' she told me. 'It is only that I

know the words by heart and pretend to read. That is the
duty of a teacher. I would so like to learn how to read
and write, señora, to instruct those who are growing up
like heathens without the wisdom of the Church.'

'But if I teach you,' I bargained, 'you must also learn
such ordinary words as broom and mop, and beans and
tortillas, that you may go to market alone with a list in
your hand.'

You bounded up, Ofelia, as if Heaven could not offer
more! And I saw shining in your face, besides the zeal
of the nun, the joy of one who knows perfect servanthood.
But it was slow, hard work, and I bitterly regretted my
bargain; for it took a whole morning for the precious
market list to be written. As for the chickens that started
all this, they sickened and died sometime later, one by
one. And since there had been nothing with which to
feed them, and since Manolo did not wish them to live
anyway, it seemed the best thing that could happen, and
the Escotos accepted it without much grief.

Rain-scape

MANOLO kept the grocery on the corner, and when I had called him a gachupín I was glad that Ofelia did not understand. When Mexico was a colony of Spain, the Indians called the Spaniards who came there gachupínes. The word means 'spurs' — the spurs that the Spaniards wore when on horseback, the spurs of their fierce cruelty toward the Indians. Today the term is still used for those Spaniards who come to Mexico looking on it as a barbarous country, but who come to make money and then to go back with it to Spain. It is a word not to be used lightly, for it may start a fight. The Mexicans say that all the groceries are in the hands of gachupínes; and certainly I never went into one — the prosperous big corner stores, and not the sad little stalls where candles and rope-ends are sold —

without hearing the lisping speech of the old-world Spaniard. Manolo, then, was a gachupín, and yet a fine fellow in everything but business. He would not stand for competition, and besides the big corner grocery he kept the bakery next to it, and ran and unlocked it whenever his customers asked for rolls. The neighborhood was growing fast, and there were rumors that he would open a meat store too. So that there was no doubt that when all the houses were built, Manolo would be the biggest local merchant and a power in the community. He lived on the ground floor, and the patio where he lived was filled with birds, in which he took great delight. He had a buxom wife and a red-headed baby and a fine voice. On Sundays I used to hear him sing — not the songs of Mexico but the strange, twisting airs of his native Andalusia. And I thought how it had needed the Moors in Spain and the Spaniards in Mexico, to hear those songs of a Sunday morning.

A German couple lived under me. I had greeted them on the stairs, but I did not know them. Looking down into their window I could see papers laid out with bugs on them. So I decided they must be entomologists, which seemed very plausible for a German couple. Then there were the lawyer and his wife in the front apartment. Mexico is full of lawyers without any clients, and he seemed to be one of them. He was home all day, and played the guitar and sang, though not so well as Manolo. But even if he had no clients, he was always given his title, according to Mexican custom. It was: 'Good morning, licenciado.' 'Come in, licenciado.' 'How is your wife, licenciado?' His wife was expecting a baby. She was small and dark, rouged and painted, overdressed and perfumed. Every morning she went to church, wearing a black veil and with a prayer-book in her hand.

The licenciado and his wife had a maid whom it was a delight to see in the morning when she came down from her room on the roof, washed and combed. She was not merely clean, she was burnished. Her black hair and golden skin caught the light like metal. And she was handsome, with marked eyebrows and a vivid smile. She had a little girl called Nicolausa. Nicolausa sat on the stairs all day, bewitching everyone who passed. She was even prettier than her mother and already, with her four-year-old charms, she could break a man's heart. She was a siren, an enchantress, and if the stairs had been rocks with ships going by, the place would have been strewn with wrecks. Surely Nicolausa knew, when she smiled showing all her tiny white teeth, that she was irresistible. And when her hair was combed in three fat braids and tied artfully over her forehead, she seemed the very incarnation of the mujercita, the little woman — in Mexico a term of sexual affection, and not as with us a vaudeville joke.

There was always some young man stealing up the stairs to see Nicolausa's mother. He would talk to her while she did the washing on the roof, her hair shining blue-black in the sun. But none of these young fellows seemed to be Nicolausa's father. I asked Ofelia whether the child had a father, and she said, thoughtfully considering, 'No, I believe not,' as one who takes it for granted that there may be children with mothers, but no fathers.

Mexico City has thousands of children whose fathers have abandoned the home, and many more who are utterly homeless. They live on the streets, ragged little urchins, prematurely old in face, precocious in vice; and because they are such distorted queer dwarfed copies of adults, tourists like to look at them and murmur, 'How cute!' They are the bootblacks who stand outside the hotels, calling 'Grasa' for the Mexicans, and 'Shine' for the Americans; and the 'cryers' who run through the streets hoarsely croaking the afternoon papers. In the afternoon one cannot pass through the first street of Bucareli where the 'cryers' gather, waiting for the big papers to issue their scurrilous afternoon editions. There is always a horde of them, barefoot, dirty, ragged to the point of nakedness; and they fight and gamble and abuse the passers-by. When the papers come out, there is a frenzied dispersal, and they rush through the streets yelling insanely, and board busses and invade restaurants; and because of this ragged maniacal army of 'cryers' all the news of the world seems evil.

The children sell lottery tickets, frequent saloons and the cheap movies, deal in drugs and stolen goods. And they accept the open obscenities of the Guatemotzin, the prostitutes' street, with calm and a cynical foul word. If you frequent the poorer restaurants you learn that they are very hungry. They come in and want to shine your shoes or sell you a lottery ticket. But if you don't want a shine or a lottery ticket, then they beg for the roll on your plate or the leavings of your meal; and if the waitress is kind, she will wait until they have scavenged to satiety before removing the dishes.

There was one child who came in regularly at El Chino's,

on the Avenida Júarez. He never bothered with pre-
liminaries. He came in to eat and that was all. First, he
would beg the waitress for permission to scavenge, whining
and twisting his face — a necessary business. But when
he had finished scavenging he was a changed man. He
set his cap defiantly, thanked the waitress with a royal
air, and walked out like one who has dined well at his
favorite club. Someone has said that if you like horses
you should not go to bullfights. And if you like children,
perhaps you should not go to Mexico City.

These homeless children do not exist because their
parents are Mexicans nor because of the Mexican Revolution. They are the fine flower of the four hundred years
of Mexican history since the conquest. For four hundred
years Mexicans have been exploited, despoiled and plun-
dered, from the time when Cortés and his men, fleeing the
wrath of the Aztecs, set to work and loaded themselves
with all the gold in Montezuma's palace, through three
centuries more when other conquerors came with the sur-
veying rod and oil drill, to rob the Mexicans of their land
and its resources, of their lives and their happiness. And
the Revolution is the protest against this, the return to
decency. As a revolution it is too big for the landowners
and too small for the communists; but it will do, if permitted to take its course, to bring decent homes, decent
food, and decent wages to Mexico's twenty million, most
of whom now lack all these things. If the Revolution
accomplishes this, it will solve the problem of the homeless children; but not the problem of the children who now
roam the streets, the blighted generation of a diseased,
undernourished, blighted parent stock. It is too late for

them. But the hope is that in the future there will no longer be such homeless children, nor districts in the city where one sees no child over five, because at that age they abandon the unspeakable hovels where they live to fend for themselves on the streets.

This is the belief of Manrique, who is a revolutionary — not one who mouths the word lightly and for his own ends, of which Mexico has many. Manrique fought in the Revolution and he remembers the years of bloodshed and violence. Now he is in his forties — tall, thin, scholarly, and somewhat sad, and still serving the cause for which he fought, humbly and prosaically in the classroom. For he believes that education is the redeeming force, the indispensable agent in shaping the future Mexico. Manrique delights in winning a child for the public schools, as though he were a priest winning a soul. He does not think that Ofelia's learning to write words like broom and mop is sufficient. He believes she should be in school, learning that Mexico is a nation and that she is part of it.

Ofelia knows so little about her country that when I told her Mexico had oceans on each side of it she was surprised, as if she had never thought of Mexico as part of the earth with definite limits; and I had to explain to her the meaning of boundaries and about the twenty-eight states of Mexico and their capitals. She received this information with polite attention, but with a definite look of skepticism. The Mexico beyond her tierra of Atotonilco was unreal, a difficult idea to grasp, something that queer Americans talked about. Even the city itself was unreal. She went to church and she went to market, for the necessities of body and soul. But she had been to the city

proper, the modern heart of the city which Mexicans call
'el centro,' only once. This was to attend a special Mass
in the Cathedral on the Great Plaza. And afterward Papa
Escoto had rushed the whole family home, as if the evil
influences of the city thickened and grew stronger at its
center. And there might be an excursion to Chapultepec
on a Sunday, when the whole family got dressed up —
Señor Escoto in clean blue overalls and the women in their
best black rebozos — and marched in a restrained procession to the park, to climb the pleasant shaded stone steps
to the castle where Maximilian and Carlota once lived.
But these were excursions of the whole tribe, including the
aunts and the little grandmother, a carefully sheltered
pleasure and a simple one; for the Mexicans spend their
afternoon at the castle sitting on the marble benches, and
gazing toward the mountains and saying ever so often,
'Qué bonito!' — 'How pretty!' Only Daniel went around
alone, having reached the mature age of sixteen, and
having, in addition, a sweetheart. Though he was last to
come to the city, he very soon appeared in city clothes
and in a city hat. But only for Sundays, and then for
just a few hours.

The rains began soon after Daniel came. They began
early and in full force, and then it was harder to get rid
of Ofelia when her work was done.

'Well, señora, it is going to rain,' she would announce,
looking at the angry froth of purple clouds in the eastern
sky.

'Then you must hurry and get home.'

'I will be caught in the rain.'

'But you have only three steps to go.'

'Yes, but the rains will catch me.'

And while we argued the rain came, the thunderous drumming incontinent downpour which may last ten minutes or the whole afternoon. This is the spring of Mexico, the rainy season that ends the long golden monotony of the dry months. But it is no pleasant spring of burgeoning trees and greening lawns. It is not a season for a poet, but one for priests and a primitive religion; for the rains come with elemental force, scourging the earth wrathfully each day.

If you must be caught in the rain, be caught in the market-place. It is like seeing the approach of doom. The peddlers wait until the last minute under the livid sky, and their cries sound far away and faint against the roll of thunder. Then the first drops fall and there is a frantic rout, a folding of tents, dumping of vegetables, and scurrying away, and in the next minute nothing but the empty streets awash like a ship in a storm, and desolate as if humanity had never been there.

Or watch the rain from under a tree on the Reforma, where you will be thoroughly drenched but unable to move, because the rain is an impenetrable wall around you. It thunders down in white spears, with a roar of wind in which the palm trees flail like straws; and blots out the world, and there is only a solitary charro on horseback, a black silhouette against the rain. He sits under his poncho, becalmed, and you think the rain must have beaten horse and rider to death. But then the white spears thin out, the air grows lighter and the rain darker, the sun appears and the charro rides away, his wet poncho shining.

I liked the rainy season better than the dry, because I like weather better than climate. The dry season is a golden vacuum; but the rainy season has change, which is weather. And while climate may create a race, weather creates the temper and sensibility of the individual. Most mornings were still clear, with a blue sky more brilliant than ever. But there were some that were dull and pleasantly clouded with premonition of the rain. And the skies that came before and after each day's cloudburst were, so to speak, not of this earth.

Perhaps it is the rarefied atmosphere that gives the clouds their solidity, their depth and effulgence of color. They rise from the mountains in the early afternoon and fill the sky, inexhaustible as chaos, sweeping the earth with a splendor of shafted light. Slowly the hot white masses and purple depths begin to lose color. A livid gray suffuses and melts them, and then the rain rips from a sky grown hard and opaque as metal. I would look down and see Señor Escoto and the other men of the lot frantically trying to keep the rain from flooding the huts. They put old newspapers on the roofs and weighted them with stones, but it did not help.

'The whole house got wet,' Ofelia would report, making it harder for me to send her away. So she stayed in the rainy afternoons, and sewed and sang the song of Atotonilco, her tierra. 'In that Atotonilco the orange trees are in flower, the maidens appear like little angels of God. Now the season makes my heart leap. Ay, 'Totonilco!' She talked endlessly of her tierra, and often illustrated a point by saying wisely: 'And therefore our song says ...' And then she sang a new song, but usually too much off key for me to get the melody. And we sang 'La Adelita,' the song of the Revolution, which Mexicans do not sing much now, though Americans like to bawl it in cantinas, beating out the time with their beer mugs.

> 'There in the depth of a wild mountain pass,
> A regiment found itself encamped;
> And a valiant maiden followed it,
> Madly enamoured of a sergeant.'

This maiden was Adelita, who was pretty as well as valiant, very popular with the troop and respected even by the colonel. It is a long story, romantic and sad, and capable of going on forever, if one is to sing all the verses that have ever been written. But Ofelia always paused thoughtfully after the stanza where the sergeant, going forth to battle, begs Adelita to weep for him with her own eyes.

'Just imagine, señora,' she said once while the song still echoed in the room. 'There was a man in my tierra who was the sweetheart of Adelita.'

'But do you think she really lived?'

'Obviously, for there is the song about her. And besides, this man was her sweetheart.'

'And what happened?'

'Well, she wanted to marry him, but this man did not care for her.'

'How strange!'

'Of course, for she was very beautiful. I certainly would have married her. But this man did not care for her, which shows how stupid he was. Qué tortuga!' she said contemptuously, of the man who had spurned Adelita. 'What a turtle! And now he is old, oh very old, and no one would think of marrying him.'

She sewed thoughtfully for a while and then asked me, trying to contain her laughter, 'Do you know the name of Manolo's clerk?'

'Never thought of it.'

'It is' — she burst out giggling — 'Edouardo!'

'Well, that's a nice name.'

'Sí? De veras? — Really?' she mocked, giggling until the tears came to her eyes. 'Edouardo!' she repeated lingeringly. 'Ed-ou-ardo!' and then she wiped her eyes and began to sew again.

'And do you know, señora, that Nicolausa's mother has a sweetheart?'

'Well, I thought she had many.'

'Oh no. She now has a very special one. She goes out to meet him every night. But he is very ugly. He has a snout like this' — she stuck out her lower lip. 'I would never choose such an ugly sweetheart.'

'And is Edouardo good-looking?'

She went off into giggles again. 'He chases me out of the store. He's very nasty. But I have made him chase me all the way into the hall here.'

'And then what happened?'

'Pues, nada. I only wanted him to chase me. Do you know, señora, I think you ought to get married.'

'Really!'

'Yes, really! I have been thinking you should marry a mordelon, because then you would be rich and also you could ride on his motor-cycle.'

'But what's a mordelon?' I asked.

She looked at me mischievously. 'Well, there is one who flirts with me on the Reforma when I go to church.

But I answer him with vulgarities, for that is the only way to shame them. They are very presuming, señora. Because of their uniforms and their motor-cycles. And because, of every bite that they take, they swallow some, and so they always have money and are very forward with the girls.'

Then I understood. My mordelon was literally 'the big biter,' the representative of the law who fines the unwary motorist on the Reforma.

'Yes, señora, they swallow most of the bites and are quite rich. You couldn't do better, señora, really. And I could get you one from the Reforma very easily. I would simply crook my finger thus, and smile at him, and tell him there's an Americana who would like to meet him. Well ... do you want it arranged?'

'Oh, by all means.' And long after I had forgotten about my mordelon, she would come rushing up the stairs, quite breathless, to tell me she had just seen one on his motor-cycle, only he went by so fast that she could not catch him for me. Still, she said, I must not lose hope.

'From This We Must Forge a Nation'

I WAS wrong about the German couple. They were not entomologists. They made chocolate for a living, and they were refugees, very homesick for the Germany they had fled from. Ernst was a musician. He played the viola, and when I heard him playing I knew that I must shut all my windows when I played the violin. Comparisons are odious. One day Ernst met me in the hall, looked at me from behind his glasses, and said: 'You play abominably. And you play the same thing over and over, until I go crazy. Haven't you any music?'

I said that I hadn't, and he offered to lend me some. 'For my own sanity,' he explained, eyeing me fiercely. 'And don't play that first exercise of Kreutzer so much.

You'll wear it away.' He leaned his viola case against the wall, and loosed a quite detached pedagogic chuckle. 'Now let's see your fingers.'

He studied my fingers, really like an entomologist examining a specimen, I thought. 'Ach — calluses!' He was thoroughly pleased. 'The French school! Your fingers hit the strings like — like —' His terrible Spanish halted and collapsed.

'Like sledgehammers,' I furnished blandly, but he went on with undiminished ferocity.

'Relax! Relax when you play. Why play the violin if you feel like choking it?'

'Why, indeed?' I echoed mentally, while his wife joined us.

She was younger than Ernst, and pretty, with cornflower hair turning gray. 'Don't mind Ernst,' she said pleasantly, in English as bad as his Spanish. 'He is very aufgeregt.'

Ernst turned on her a lamb-like look for the merest second. Then his face grew fierce again, he raised his arms and his voice broke despairingly. 'But she plays so abominably. Ach, Gott! And we are neighbors.'

'Sh — Ernst! Perhaps the fraülein understands German.' In dumb show she indicated that he must not be taken seriously. He was very nervous. 'It's the climate,' she whispered. 'He suffers much here. He has nosebleeds.'

'She needs instruction,' Ernst said.

'She will have instruction. You will come, won't you, to take lessons from Ernst? It will really make him very happy. He has not had a pupil here in Mexico.'

I nodded rather reluctantly.

'You need not pay,' she said, pushing Ernst toward the door. 'Only come, come because it will make him so happy.'

They went out, and Ernst looked back at me with the lamb-like expression that seemed always to replace his ferocity. He smiled quite shyly. 'Yes, you will come,' he said, very pleased. 'And now — now I go to play chamber music.'

I went upstairs thinking about them, and for some reason they made me feel very sad.

There was always coffee after the lesson, and I learned to play less abominably, and Ernst grew lamb-like more often, which was his natural state except when one played badly. Then he could be bravo, muy bravo, in the way the Mexicans use the word of an irritated animal, wild and ready to attack.

'Look,' he would explode. 'You play like the senile old violist in the orchestra in Germany.' He sat down with his instrument, dropped his elbow to his knee, smiled inanely and crossed his eyes, and then began to bow the strings with horrible feebleness. 'Yes,' he nodded. 'That's how he plays, and there's one in every orchestra, but the conductor can't fire him out of pity. And he can't play, he can't play any more.' He continued nodding his head, staring before him, and then he got up and wiped his face and I saw that beads of sweat had come out on his forehead.

'You!' he said angrily. 'You do not have to stir chocolate all day, and yet you cannot play.' He started a movement of the Beethoven concerto with a sweep and sonority of tone that brought Lutzie to the door, listening to him.

'If only he could practice,' she told me sadly. 'If only there were more music in Mexico. But he must stand all day making the chocolate, and then I must go to the German stores to sell it, and the men put their hands heavily on my shoulder and say, "But of course you are not Jews, because we do not want Jewish chocolate." And I lie and say no, we are not Jews. It is bitter bread, my child, bitter bread.'

I used to go up to the little room on the roof where they made the chocolate and help Ernst sometimes. They had all sorts of pots and pans that they had brought from Germany, and grinding and pounding machines, and everything was kept as sparklingly clean as the machinery on a ship. Everything had to be 'sauber' — clean. 'Sauber' was their god, their standard of right and wrong. A thing was or was not sauber. That was all that mattered about it. A person was or was not sauber. The floor in their apartment sparkled like gold, and their huge pillows and feather-bed bulged in the windows every morning, taking the sun; and they wore themselves thin and ill keeping things sauber, down to the last nail, the smallest cranny. That was why they did not like the Escotos. They were not sauber. When they talked to me of the Escotos it was always in German, as if only that language had the words they needed.

'And the señor is ekelhaft faul!' Ernst would splutter. 'Disgustingly lazy! All day he does nothing.'

'But he works at night,' I objected.

'Works! Is that work, sitting there in his sarape half asleep? And have you noticed how he hangs around the corner all day, talking to Manolo?'

Yes, I had noticed. Señor Escoto had that Mexican way of standing for hours on one spot, relaxed and untiring, as if the air supported him comfortably; and had I not seen him on the corner I would have missed him, his smile and his greeting. But I had often wondered when he slept, and now I had my first misgiving that perhaps he was lazy. For if a man foregoes needed sleep, which it is his duty to take, in favor of loafing on a street corner, can one not say that he is lazy after all, superbly so?

'And who do you think commits all the robberies in the house?' Lutzie added. 'Who but Herr Escoto, who has a pass-key to all the apartments!'

'Do you *know* that he has one?'

'Obviously he has. For how else could he commit the robberies?'

'No, I don't believe it.'

'Child! Don't be foolish. Watch Herr Escoto, I warn you. Don't ever let him enter the apartment. And it is very wrong of you to have Ofelia there, finding out where everything is.'

I quailed guiltily before her, for I had given the Escotos a key to my apartment. Being a chronic key-forgetter, I would come home and find myself locked out. And then I would have to call Señor Escoto, and he would have to call Daniel, and they would fetch a rope and go up on the roof, and Daniel would be hoisted down over the wall, dangling perilously in the air until he managed to open my window or break it. This furnished a pleasant circus for all the women on the lot, who gathered to watch it; but I felt that such scenes reflected on the efficiency of the Americans, and must end. So I had given the Escotos a key. True, the house was subject to robberies — bold large-scale robberies that might occur in broad daylight, as if some invisible spirit made free with the apartments. But it had simply never occurred to me that they were the work of Señor Escoto. Yet under Lutzie's severe blue eye I had a moment of misgiving. And yet, I reasoned, how could he be the guilty one, if my apartment was the only one that had never been touched? And then the relentless bad logic of suspicion made me think: *But that proves it!* I reddened with anger, not at Señor Escoto, but at the Germans. And then at myself, because I remembered the gold cigarette lighter that he had used so furtively, that night of my visit to the hut when Daniel came.

'Yes, mark my words,' Lutzie was saying, 'Herr Escoto is not in order.'

Yet for all their suspicion they were good-hearted. They plied Ofelia with chocolate until she was sick, and bought dolls for Nicolausa, whom they petted and admired inordinately. It was only that cleanliness and order were the all-important virtues, and they probably would have felt themselves slipping morally had they not spent part of each day suspecting that things were not clean enough, and that their neighbors were not absolutely in order. And besides, they were in a strange land, exiled and homesick. 'Qué bonito!' Ernst would say, just like a Mexican, while he paused in the chocolate-making to look off toward the mountains. But at those times I saw in his eyes a great sadness, and perhaps the memory of another landscape, more familiar, more placid, and certainly more orderly. Then he would return to his chocolate-mixing with renewed vigor.

'Everything must be done with relaxation,' he would say, mixing away and eyeing me sternly from behind his glasses. He looked ludicrous in his long chocolate-spattered smock, and with a heavy muffler tied around his neck to protect his clean white collar. 'Whether it's making chocolate or playing the violin. Observe my arm. The power comes from the shoulder, the rest is relaxed. With relaxation one can work endlessly.'

'Then the Mexicans should accomplish a great deal,' I said. 'They are always relaxed.'

He snorted angrily. 'Ach — the Mexicans! It's not the same thing. You do not understand,' he added sadly.

But I did. This German relaxation was a strenuous matter, something to be achieved by thought and care and exercise, and not just a careless gift from the gods. At the beginning of every lesson we had to limber up first, like athletes. We would take our places facing the wall, I with my violin and Ernst with his viola. Then, at a signal, we lifted our instruments, braced them against the wall, and began our arm movements. There was no sound, thirty times for each exercise, finger-flexing, wrist-flexing, and woe to me if I smiled! 'Nicht lachen!' Ernst thundered. 'How can one learn to play if one is not serious?' And we continued, until Lutzie came and stood in the doorway, to look at us pityingly. 'Enough, Ernst! Let the poor child alone! After all, it is not her profession.'

'Which means nothing,' Ernst delivered himself. 'After all, you play or you don't.' But we left the wall and took up our bows.

'The action of playing the violin,' Ernst said, looking at me with his bow poised over the strings, 'is precisely like that of shooting a gun. Have you ever used a gun, fraülein?'

'Yes, once in Connecticut. We shot at empty bottles —'

'Then you understand,' he went on impatiently. 'You hold the left arm — so, just as you would a gun. And then the right arm high, as when you pull the trigger. And just as you would sight the target, the head must be so, facing front. Now! Let me see.'

I tried it, and he said it was very good. And thus, with this military send-off, we launched into the graceful andante of Mozart's 'Nacht-musik.' We were going through it in preparation for the first meeting of the orchestra. Ernst and some other German refugees were starting one, and I would be allowed to play second fiddle.

One morning our playing was really interrupted by a sound as of shooting. We rushed to the window and saw the peons who worked on the building across the street setting off firecrackers, throwing them into the air with such speed and energy that one would have thought their lives depended on it. The firecrackers zoomed into the blue sky, exploded with little puffs of white smoke. Soon the sound came from other buildings, from other streets, from all over the city. It was deafening, as if the city were under bombardment. Downstairs we found all the people from the lots gathered outside Manolo's store. 'Qué bonito!' they said, looking up and admiring the smoke of battle that drifted over the houses. 'And the cross, qué bonito!' On the roof of the building the peons had erected a wooden cross splendidly festooned with colored paper ribbons and ivy wreaths. 'To bless the new work,' Edouardo explained.

There was much drinking on all the unfinished buildings through the rest of the day, and the explosions of firecrackers kept booming over the city and did not die out until late afternoon. And then came another sound — the siren of the ambulances going to pick up the workers who had fallen off the buildings. But by night it was quiet, with only the wind rustling the paper ribbons on the crosses, a mysterious sound as if pagan gods were abroad. Every unfinished building in the city had its cross, even the steel skeletons of the skyscrapers in the center of town; though Ofelia was sure that none could be as splendid as the one Daniel had made for the building where he watched. Coming home late one night I went out of my way to see it. The cross was there, but not Daniel. Then something moved in the shadows. It was Daniel with his sweetheart. He held her hand and they went into the darkness of the building, treading carefully over the rubble-strewn floor. Yet when I reached home I saw his sweetheart come from the lot and walk toward Manolo's store. It troubled me as I went upstairs. How could she have reached the lot as quickly as I did? I would have heard her if she had followed me. But I had come down the dark street alone, hearing only the sound of the wind rustling through the crosses.

'I suppose Daniel will get married soon,' I remarked to Ofelia, on the afternoon following when the rain had imprisoned us.

She considered. 'We do not know, señora. He is very camote.'

I reached for the dictionary, a business that never failed to amuse her. Camote: sweet-potato.

'And what does it mean to be camote?'

'Pues, nowadays,' she said sagely, 'all the young men are very camote. They lack responsibility, señora, and think only of their own good times.' She sighed as one who had known many betrayals, though actually her interest in such matters had passed. She had forgotten about Edouardo and the mordelon, for this was the period of the fairy tales. Every day she told me the fairy tales she had heard in her tierra. They were Puss-in-Boots, Snow-White, and all the old tales over again, only enchantingly disguised. The good fairy was always the Virgin of Guadalupe, who appeared in all her splendor at the right moments. And the poor princess was set to grinding corn at the metate instead of spinning; and Red Riding Hood carried gifts of tortillas and chile to her grandmother, and even the little rabbit did not have his cabbage patch, but was caught stealing black beans. Then she told me of the ghosts that haunted the night roads of her tierra. The ghosts, however, were quite native. Ofelia had not seen any, but her father and mother had seen them often. They were not even decent ghosts, but 'espantos' — frightful things.

'And does your mother see them here in the city?'

'Pues, sí!' she said. 'Only the other night —' And it was a tale to curdle one's blood. There were also serpents that fell with the rain. She told me one had fallen in the house just a few days ago, visible to all and causing great consternation. Then she added with a luxurious shudder: 'Qué horror!'

I had to typewrite all the fairy tales for her, for the typewriter fascinated her. Already she could read a little, and when she took the paper in her hand, and, knowing the story, was able to read it, she was overawed as if at a miracle — that the paper could indeed give back the fairy tale to her.

'If you could only go to school, Ofelia.'

'Yes,' she said sadly, 'but my mother would never permit it. She says the boys will lead me away and teach me bad things. But I don't care for them at all, señora. Today there were two little old men in the meat-store, and they began to jest with me, and I answered them with vulgarities — the coarsest things to say that I could think of. They shut up, then, and slunk away. And that's what I always do.'

And a very good tactic, I thought. 'But if you went to school, you might become a teacher.'

'No, señora.' She was proudly resigned. 'I cannot think of that. Besides, they teach evil things in the schools. That is what the priest said. No, señora, I am content to be a maid. Only I would so like to wear a real maid's apron. My aunt and I saw the loveliest ones in the market at Santa Julia, just like those they wear on the Reforma, and very cheap. We went there to buy shoes for Saint Pancracio, he who was martyred so young.'

'Ofelia! You didn't spend your last salary on shoes for the saint!'

'In the end, no,' she remembered, sighing. 'Think of it. We looked all over the Santa Julia market, and then we went to the Merced, and then to the market of Tacubaya, looking for little white shoes with red ribbons. But they

were all too expensive, as a result of which we could not
buy them.'

'But you need shoes more than the saint!'

She looked at me a moment as if undecided whether to
be shocked, and then it struck her as a very witty thing
I had said, and she giggled appreciatively. But the more
she thought about it, the wittier it seemed — this juxta-
position of her need and the saint's. And long after, I
would hear her repeating the words softly to herself, and
inwardly laughing.

'Now, Ofelia, you are going to meet Manrique,' I said
firmly. 'This very night when he comes here.'

'El maestro?'

'El maestro.'

She looked aghast. The idea of meeting him terrified
her because, as a teacher, he represented that authority to
which she was truant. 'No, señora, please —'

But all her pleadings and excuses did not help. Manrique came punctually as usual, for he prided himself on
having an American consciousness of the time. And when
she stood before him with her back pressed against the
wall, as if she might find a miraculous escape through it,
he looked at her and said: 'You come from the lowland.'

She nodded her head, but she would not look up.

'And I will tell you the very part of the lowland that
you come from,' Manrique continued, while Ofelia eyed
him sideways, beguiled by this divination.

'You come from Jalisco.'

'Yes,' she said.

'And I will tell you the very village in Jalisco that you
come from. It is Atotonilco.'

Her eyes widened and she looked up smiling. 'Pues, sí! That is my pueblo.'

'It is a region of valiant men and beautiful women. Proverbial,' Manrique said, 'the reputation of the men for valor, and of the women for beauty.'

'Do you hear, Ofelia, what el maestro says of your tierra?'

'Yes, señora.'

'But they are conservative,' he went on, shaking his head. 'Very conservative. They sigh for the times of Porfirio Díaz. They are not with us in the Revolution.'

'But Ofelia knows nothing of the Revolution . . .'

'Oh, but I do, señora.' She was suddenly voluble. 'For my mother speaks of it often. How the federals came from one side and the rebels came from the other, and there was much shooting and people were murdered and hung from the trees. It was bad, señora, very bad.'

'We had to win our freedom in blood and violence,' Manrique said with a sad reasonableness, while Ofelia looked at him, wide-eyed. 'But now there are schools. Schools for you, Ofelia.' He took off his glasses, wiped them and put them back, and his face grew stern as he leaned forward to her. 'You must go to school, Ofelia, do you hear? You must go to school.'

There was such intensity in his voice and such sternness in his face that she shrank away from him, covered her eyes and burst into tears.

'I know, I know,' she wept, in an extremity of confession. 'I am ashamed, I am ashamed that I do not go to school.' And not all our coaxing could make her stop crying or look up again.

'Ofelia!' Manrique said, more gently. 'Ofelia...' But she drew away from him, crying bitterly. He shook his head, looking utterly sad and defeated; and though he did not speak I knew what the words would have been, for I had heard them often: 'There, you see? That is our problem. They will not come to the schools. There are so many that we cannot reach, so many...'

Later I asked him how he had guessed so exactly where Ofelia came from. 'There is nothing to it,' he said, with a self-deprecatory smile. 'One can usually tell, because we Mexicans are not one race. We are still a people of tribes, as we were before the conquest. There were many different Indian tribes before the conquest, and the blood of the conquerors was only a few drops in an ocean. The blood of others too — the negroes, the Chinese, the French — how we are mixed, and yet we are still mostly Indian. Our faces' — he stroked his own by way of demonstration — 'are still Aztec or Otomí, or Mayan or Zapotecan, or whatever you wish. The other blood only made the variations and gave some differences of speech and gesture. I have traveled all over my country, and I know what face and speech come from each region. And the region also leaves its stamp — the hot and the cold, the dry or wet, mountain and desert and jungle — these, too, have formed us with an endless variety of climate and conditions.'

He was silent a moment. 'Yes, señorita,' he concluded rather sadly. 'From this we must forge a nation, from these tribes and from this variety.'

The Stupid Otomís

I REMEMBERED his words a few days later, as I walked on the road to Ixmiquilpan, in the Valley of the Mesquite where the Otomís live. On each side of the road I saw their grass huts. They are built so small that one must enter them stooping, and the eye can hardly distinguish them in the fields from the growths of cactus and mesquite. Looking at the parched fields and the mountains beyond — the strange mountains where the barren rock burned purple in the sun — I remembered Manrique's words: We are various, formed by mountain and desert. Here were mountain and desert, the barren Valley of the Mesquite, the blighted land to which the Otomís fled, a conquered people long before the coming of the Spaniards. And here in the Valley of the Mesquite they had been formed, through four hundred years of desert poverty.

It was Monday, and the Otomís were going to market. They streamed in from the fields and swarmed on the highway, a small earth-brown people, barefoot and ragged, bringing their poor produce to the plaza at Ixmiquilpan. They brought tunas, the watery fruit of the nopal, and beans and charcoal and cloths woven of maguey fiber. Long before the conquest the Otomís were famous as weavers of this cloth, and they roamed far and wide as merchants of it. And today it is still their most important product, their only form of commerce with the outside world. Now, as they came in from the fields, many of them — men and women alike — carried a distaff on the shoulder, deftly spinning the fiber of maguey as they trudged to market.

Without the maguey plant the Otomís could not live. It gives a tall stalk for making their huts, and a dry grass for fuel, and a fiber for spinning. It is shelter and warmth, and clothing and commerce. It is food and water too, for it gives the juice from which pulque is made. In the Valley of the Mesquite there is no water for drinking. From Mexico City the black polluted waters of the canals drain into the valley; but of this black water the Otomís say: 'Boil it, boil it again, and boil it a third time. Then throw it away and take your drink of pulque.' An Otomí laborer working on the haciendas receives half of his wages in pulque — half of the forty centavos that he gets for working from dawn to dark. It is wages in death, for, though pulque gives nourishment and strength to work for a time, it brings in the end weakness and disease and death.

Land without water! When I had left the highway and

entered the streets of Ixmiquilpan, I walked ankle-deep
in soft immemorial dust. The air itself was dusty, and
even the mountains looming beyond the plaza seemed
made of dust, an eternity of dust for the dry air to feed
on. Land without water, as though Creation had faltered
and given of only one element — a land that awaits the
bridegroom. And because there is no water one thinks
constantly of the sea. There, beyond that dip in the mountains, there is a stretch of sky that looks like the sea! But
it is a mirage, the wish-fulfillment of the eyes tired of dust.

There are five thousand Otomís in the Valley of the
Mesquite, only a few of the hundreds of thousands in all
Mexico. All do not live in the poverty of those in the
Valley of the Mesquite. An agricultural people before the
Aztecs conquered them and drove them from the fertile
lands, they are now good agriculturists wherever they
have land that will yield. And with the Otomís there are
about five million Indians of different tribes, and more
than that number of mestizos who live under the same
cultural and economic conditions as the Indians. They
form the great majority of Mexico's population.

Since the Revolution there have been many slogans for
redeeming the Indian. He would be incorporated to
civilization, or civilization would be incorporated to him.
But now the economic needs of the country have acted as
a solvent on slogans. The Indians are recognized as the
great mass of the rural population, the 'arms' that must
bring Mexico's backward agriculture to more abundance.
So that their education has become a double-edged sword.
A greater abundance in their lives means greater abundance for the country — a double-edged sword or a benign

circle. That is the dream of the young revolutionaries who go as teachers to the remote hidden pueblos, to the malaria-ridden sierras. No facile dream, for the roll of rural school-teachers has its martyrs.

I had come to Ixmiquilpan the night before and stayed in the not very palatial Hotel Palacio. At night the town had been deserted and an air of desolation hung over the lampless, dusty streets. But now in the morning I walked through a crowded plaza, looking for Señor Rios who had shown me the school. I found him in a booth taking refrescos. 'What have you bought?' he greeted me. 'Pues, nada.' 'You must buy a woven sash and an ayate — a woven bag. The Otomís are great weavers.' There were a few boys from the school with him. They looked very workmanlike in their blue overalls, and they were alert and smiling — a different race from the Otomís who sat beside their wares in the market.

There had been no classes that day, for the market-day is all-important, no more to be violated than a religious festival. It would be a day of diversion for them — bathing in a little stream and then practice for the band. Later they would go back to the school in the Government truck. It stood waiting in the plaza, a very large truck lettered: 'Department of Indigenous Affairs' — and a novelty in Ixmiquilpan where only the bus comes and a rare tourist car. Nor is there any motion-picture house either. There is an old theater that flourished in colonial times, but now it is used only for political meetings. And there are no newspapers. 'But what good are newspapers in Spanish,' said Señor Rios, 'if the Otomís cannot read them? We are going to have a newspaper in Otomí,' he

said, and the boys smiled slowly, as if they were not quite
sure that this would be right. We sat in the booth, eating pink air-blown ices and talking of the school.

'But there is one thing I should like to know,' I said.
'Do the Otomís who live across the road from the school,
those whose huts are so near ... Do they ever cross the
road to ask your help in anything?'

'No,' he said slowly, and he seemed disturbed. 'No,
that is the trouble. We have chosen the pupils of the
school from all the Otomí regions, the brightest and most
ambitious ones we could find. We teach them the best
methods of cultivation, we teach them Spanish, and try
to make them part of our national life. But we must reach
the people themselves, we must arouse their curiosity and
their will to better themselves — the will broken by so
many centuries of poverty and exploitation. They have
left their mark. But first must come land — land of their
own, and water. That is basic. And then, of course, better
houses — houses in which they can stand upright; and a
diet other than pulque, and the fight against malaria, and
then ... ' He fell silent, looking past the busy plaza to
the mountains. 'There are no limits,' he said, 'no limits
to the richness of life that we may forge for ourselves here
in Mexico.' He returned to his ices and then, as if abashed,
he suddenly raised his voice calling to a boy in the plaza.
'Hey, you, Mario! That you fetch me some quinine in the
pharmacy. I have malaria,' he explained apologetically.
'I was careless and forgot to take quinine on a trip up
there in the mountains. It's bad because it breaks the
faith of the pupils in medicine. It's a bad example,' he
added.

He had started to tell me about the Otomí superstitions about malaria when a furious hornblowing sounded from the bus that was going back to Mexico City, and I had to rush to the Hotel Palacio to get my things. Don Jacinto, the proprietor, was still playing dominoes with his cronies in the patio. He rose to help me with my bags.

'And did you see the town, señorita?'

'Yes, I saw the town.'

'Pues' — he shrugged — 'there is not much to see here. Here there are not the beauties of Mexico, which so attract your countrymen. But perhaps you will tell your countrymen about the Hotel Palacio?'

I nodded, waiting for the bus which had disappeared on the other side of the plaza, and Don Jacinto continued with the firmness of one who must tell much in a short time.

'As you see, señorita, we are unfortunate here. We live in the midst of these Otomís, who are savages incapable of civilization. They are so' — he raised his hand to indicate the height of a child — 'of very small stature, dirty and stupid. And they do not even speak Spanish. Yet the Government tries to civilize them, at great expense and with a great waste of energy, which grieves me sufficiently. You must excuse me, señorita, for talking thus, but it has always pleased me to talk to Americans. Perhaps you will return, and then we can talk further?'

'Oh yes, I will return.'

'Ah ... then you will see, you will see,' he nodded.

'Yes, then I will see,' I said, with amiable postponement of the conclusion, which is the way to make conclusions in Mexico.

And then the bus came and I was going back to the city.

But I did not return to Ixmiquilpan as soon as I had planned, for when I came home there was a letter for me which determined the course of my life for the next four weeks. It came from the Department of Government, and the tenor of it was that they could not extend the time I might stay in Mexico. Not only that. They entertained the gravest suspicions concerning me, and I must call to see their Señor X, in order to clarify what was now designated as 'the case.' So I went immediately to the Department of Government to see Señor X, and found him very gentle and courteous, but rather terrifying too. He had a dark beauty and soft reptilian eyes, and he could stare at one for minutes at a time, unblinkingly, in a way that was thoroughly disconcerting.

'Señorita,' he said softly, 'I am afraid that we suspect that you are a Polish refugee.'

I looked at him dazedly for a second, and then I heard myself denying it in that floundering, helpless way in which one denies the utterly impossible.

'Nevertheless,' Señor X repeated, 'we suspect that you are a Polish refugee without the legal permission to be here in Mexico.'

'I assure you,' I said, but weakly and without conviction, 'I am not a Polish refugee.'

'You deny it, señorita?'

'I deny it.'

'You would say that you are not what we suspect you to be?'

'I would say that I am not, señor.'

He leaned back with half-closed eyes, and seemed to pass into deep thought. 'I might tell you, señorita, that your status is perilous, for we shall be obliged to return you to Poland if our suspicions should be confirmed. However, if you could present strong evidence to the contrary ...' He opened his eyes and looked directly at me. 'Have you a birth certificate, señorita?'

'Certainly, señor.' And I began to look feverishly in my purse, while he fixed me with his unblinking stare. I found everything else, but not the birth certificate. 'It must be at home,' I told him weakly. 'I shall bring it this afternoon.'

'No need to rush yourself,' Señor X relented in a kind of treacherous, feline way. 'Tomorrow will do. Tomorrow I will be waiting for you,' he added softly, and bowed me out.

I was really disturbed, because I had tangled with Mexican bureaucracy before. It is not that they are martinets, insisting on a strict observance of all the forms. Quite the contrary. They delight in flouting the facts, they love to spin fantasies. They love rearranging reality, and they will insist that a thing is so (when it obviously is not), or not so (when it obviously is), with the sweet, gentle, and terrible insistence of the quietly insane. I remembered the time when I had entered Mexico. I was the only passenger on the bus, at night from San Antonio to Laredo, and the driver and I talked, and he could not understand why I was going to Mexico. 'Remember,' he said, 'Uncle Sam takes his protecting arm off your shoulder when you cross the border.'

It is not that Uncle Sam withdraws his protecting arm

when you cross the border, for no one needs protection in Mexico. But what one loses in crossing the border is Uncle Sam's Anglo-Saxon calm and reasonableness. One enters an Alice-in-Wonderland world, a world of Latin logic — or Latin illogic as one may prefer to call it. I found that out as soon as I reached the border. It was midnight, I was the only one crossing into Mexico, I had ten minutes to make the train, and the Mexican official at the bridge knew this.

'What is this?' he asked, eyeing my tourist card as though I had shown him some rare but dangerous insect.

'It is my tourist card.'

'You claim to be an American citizen, señorita?'

'I do not claim it. I have proved it to the satisfaction of the Mexican consul in New York, who gave me this card.'

He sighed and looked at the clock. The train was whistling impatiently. 'Unfortunately, señorita, consuls are not infallible. It is quite likely that he made a mistake.'

'But I showed him this, my birth certificate.' And I laid the photostatic copy of it on his desk.

'What is this?' he asked, peering at it, and then his eyes wandered to the clock with a sort of joyous leer, and back to me. 'You really haven't much time, señorita. The train leaves in ten minutes.'

'I know that, and that's why I am telling you. I am an American citizen, and this is my birth certificate. It's a copy, and I paid a dollar and a half for it, and it's quite official, because — well, it's an official photostat. You know, they take a picture.' And I went through the pantomime of someone snapping a picture, because I felt sure my English did not reach him.

'Ah,' he said, watching me approvingly. 'It is a picture.'

'Yes, of my birth certificate.'

'It is the proof that you are an American citizen.'

'Yes,' I said, and then the train whistled piercingly and he looked at the clock and smiled.

'You really haven't much time, señorita,' he said reproachfully, and then he contemplated my birth certificate with a deadly, irritating calm. 'Look,' he pointed. 'It says that you live at Brook Avenue, in New York.'

'No, I was only born there.'

'But it says you live there: Brook Avenue, New York.'

'It is the place where I was born.'

'But it says: Address, Brook Avenue, New York.'

'Yes, that was my address when I was born. I have moved many times since.'

'You do not live there now?'

'No, I do not live there now. I have not lived there for a long time. One moves around after one is born.'

He crumpled a little at this, but soon rallied with a light of triumph in his eye. 'Señorita,' he sighed, shaking his head regretfully, 'it is entirely possible that you are not an American citizen. After all, a document can be forged.'

'No,' I told him patiently. 'This birth certificate is not forged. It's a photostatic copy. You know, a picture.' And I repeated my picture-taking pantomime, which he seemed to enjoy all over again. 'And the United States Government,' I added, 'would have thought it sufficient to give me a passport on it.'

I should never have said that. 'Then you have no passport, señorita?'

'Yes, I did not get one.'

'They denied you a passport?' he asked softly.

'I did not say that. I said that I did not get one, and I did not get one because I did not ask for one. Because they told me it was not necessary for entering Mexico.'

'Yes, it is not necessary for entering Mexico,' he said, and then he looked at me meaningly. 'For an American citizen, that is.'

We looked at each other with what I imagine must have been the rodent-like stare of two white mice caught in a psychologist's labyrinth. And then a great indifference overcame me. I did not care about entering Mexico any more. It was too difficult. I told the cab-driver who was taking my things across the border that it was no longer necessary, I had decided to stay in the United States. I told him to take the things back to the bus station, and I gathered up my birth certificate and began to walk away from the official desk. But the cab-driver had already been at the customs house with the baggage, and they had already gone through it and marked it 'Revisado,' and we were all in a fine predicament. He began to talk very rapidly and sternly to the official, evidently telling him that the game had gone far enough, and the official called me back and apologized in his fashion.

'You see, señorita, we must be careful. Granted that you were born an American citizen, there are still many ways by which you may have lost that status in the course of your life. For instance,' he looked at me hopefully, 'you may have married an alien?'

'I did not marry an alien,' I assured him.

'Or you may have committed a crime for which you were sent to prison?'

'That did not happen to me either.'

'I am only supposing, señorita. It is my duty to suppose these things. However'... He shrugged, then gathered himself for a solution. 'Your case is dubious, very dubious,' he said briskly, 'but I think it can still be arranged. The question of a small deposit which you will leave here at the border...'

I asked him how much it was and he mentioned a fantastic sum. And then something happened. I became an American citizen not only in fact, but in spirit. There descended on me that righteous indignation which is the characteristic of the American citizen when his right to go anywhere is questioned, when his lordship of the earth is challenged. I leaned over and banged the desk while I told him I would leave no deposit, I was not required to leave a deposit. I was an American citizen with all my papers in order, and I intended to enter Mexico then and there, and make the train if he didn't mind — or had he another idea for getting me to Mexico City? But long before I finished, he had reached for his pen and official book, while he looked at me with a mixture of awe and admiration.

'On my own responsibility, señorita,' he said, writing in his book. 'On my own responsibility I will permit you to pass.' He sighed as though he expected dire consequences.

We made the train just as it was pulling out, and the cab-driver threw my luggage on the platform and I hauled myself after it. 'They are all after money,' he had told me, as we careened toward the station. Possibly, I thought, but that could be only part of it. If I had

bribed that official he would naturally have taken it.
But I am sure he enjoyed the whole business. It was the
official game of rearranging reality.

So, remembering this, I was worried about the Department of Government, and as soon as I got home I began
to look for my birth certificate. But it was not to be found.
It had disappeared in the course of my various movings,
and therefore, according to the logic of the Department,
I was a Polish refugee. But I did not want to be deported
to Poland. I wanted to stay in Mexico.

The Escotos, whom I took into my confidence, were
deeply concerned. 'Is it the police who want you to leave?'
Mrs. Escoto asked me.

'Yes, in a manner of speaking it is the police,' I said,
for to them the Government meant the police, and
nothing else.

'They are shameless ones,' she said, shaking her head
severely. 'They always have things their own way.'

'They want money,' Señor Escoto said with finality.

But I quailed at the thought of bribing Señor X. Besides, it would be taken as my admission that I was a
Polish refugee, and the status would be fixed on me for
life. I talked it all over with some Mexican friends, and
they were quite alarmed. 'Cuidado!' they said. 'Beware!
Beware of these officials.' And then I asked them about
getting a lawyer, and they were even more alarmed.
'Cuidado!' they said. 'Beware of lawyers!' So there was
nothing to do but wait for the thing to run its course.
But meanwhile my position was perilous. For I had over-
stayed my leave, through no fault of my own, and at any
moment the Department might make another logical

somersault and decide to fine or arrest me for it. The birth certificate that was coming from the States was delayed, and each day I went to Señor X and told him it would surely come, and each day he fixed his hypnotic eyes on me and said he hoped so.

Three weeks of this, and then something happened in the dark, mysterious departmental mind. I do not know what it was, but I received a letter saying they had decided that I was not a Polish refugee after all. There was no evidence to support it, they said, and so they were pleased to withdraw their suspicions and they would henceforth accept the fact that I was an American citizen. But they saved face. In order to stay longer in Mexico, I must leave the country and re-enter. It would not inconvenience me, Señor X assured me. A mere matter of taking the bus to Laredo, walking across the international bridge, and then back again.

Do You Know the Highway?

I DID not mind, for thus I would 'know the highway.' The Mexicans are very proud of the Pan-American Highway that winds its miraculous length through the eastern sierra, and they ask every tourist, 'Do you know the highway?' And if you do not, they advise rather sternly, 'You must know it.' It is a duty, part of your experience of Mexico. And they are right. I have been over the highway four times now. I have gone in the rainy season, when the weird lunar mountain shapes were softened with green; and in the dry season when they burned with all the colors of the spectrum; and once when we drove through the whiteness of fog that would lift to show the world below us, new and startling as if this were the moment of creation. And each time it was new, breath-taking and unbelievable. It

is the nearest thing to flying without leaving the earth.
And when the view unfolds, flowing in infinite mountain
waves to the horizon, it is like witnessing that first flow
and unfolding of the earth of which geologists tell us.

Today an American company runs an auxiliary bus
service from Laredo to Mexico City; but at the time of my
first trip there was no American bus, and one traveled
Mexican. The Mayab bus was a huge antique affair
equipped with shades that did not pull down, windows
that did not open, and seats that did not spring back.
There were gadgets for doing these things, but they did
not work, which made it all very Mexican. For the Mexicans it is sufficient that they have a thing; whether it
works or not is irrelevant. They point with pride to this
or that modern device, and then they add with almost
equal pride, 'However, it doesn't function.' And when
things don't function they are not merely out-of-order
(the nice American phrase which implies just a temporary
failure). In Mexico things are 'descompuesto' — that is,
decomposed, disintegrated, fallen apart. I think they
rather relish this strong word, so pleasantly discouraging
to any effort at mending things.

After a few struggles I found out that everything on
the bus was decomposed. Even the General could not
make anything work, but he used his efforts to assist me
as an excuse to come and sit next to me. I had never
traveled with a general before, and at first I was flustered.
But then I remembered that generals are numerous in the
Mexican army, and he turned out to be a very human,
simple military man. He had fought in the Revolution
and received his rank at that time, and before that he

had been a plain, not too prosperous rancher. 'My hands are made for work,' he said, exhibiting them. 'For work in the fields.'

The General knew the highway. He knew every inch of it and he foretold every curve, every climb and descent, as if he had a map of it spread on his knees. But that wasn't enough. He loved the road so much that he felt called on to conduct the driving as though he were conducting music. 'Watch, watch!' he would say, 'now we ascend.' And he lifted his hands slowly like an orchestra leader guiding a crescendo. Then, as the ascent ended, he flourished it away and his hands played a gentle pianissimo for the level stretch. He was never wrong in his timing, never wrong in his predictions. The two young chauffeurs (there are always two chauffeurs on a Mexican bus, one to drive and the other to talk to the driver and distract him) looked around at him in awe. 'It's because I have driven over the highway so often,' the General explained loudly to the whole bus. And he was careful to add that he always drove his own car, but this time his sister had brought him to the capital, and so he must go home by bus.

I learned a great deal about the General. He was stationed in Monterrey, where he owned a beautiful home which seemed still to overwhelm him with its size and splendor. He was a widower and he had mourned his wife for longer than the prescribed Catholic year, and he would not go to dances or hear music because of his mourning. He must have been very fond of his wife, for tears came to his eyes when he spoke of her — the genuine tears of a sentimental old man. He did not think he would

marry again, he was too old for that. 'With what illusion
can I marry again?' he asked, looking at me sadly. Besides, he had a young daughter ready for marriage, and
he wanted to see her happily situated before he thought
about himself. But in spite of all this, he assured me, he
was not exactly a hermit. When we came to Monterrey,
if I conformed to the idea of stopping over, he would show
me the town and his house and introduce me to his
daughter. Also, he would show me a picture of his wife.
And when these formalities were over, we would have some
time together. He put his hand on my knee at this point,
and said: 'I do this as a sign of my esteem and respect.'
'I hope so,' I answered.

But he was really good company, and I could not wish
for a better traveling companion. He would not let me
miss the least part of the trip. He knew all the legends
connected with the highway — here was the stretch of
smooth precipitous rock known as The Mirror; here the
car of a gringa had gone hurtling over the rocks; here
there was water, but stagnant and shallow, and of no use
for irrigation. 'If we were endowed with water like your
country...' he said. He believed in Mexico for the
Mexicans, in the right of every campesino to land, and
that every laborer should share in the profits that came
from the labor of his hands. He held up his hand again
and turned his fist for display. 'Isn't it just,' he said
earnestly, 'if one's hands do the work?' And then he felt
called on to apologize for his fervor. 'These are not topics
to discuss with a lady,' he said, 'but I understand that
with you American women one may discuss anything, even
politics.' The General was active in politics. He would

not tell me which presidential candidate he supported, but he was actively campaigning on the trip. At every stop there was someone who sought him out, and the General would speak to him rapidly, giving directions for calling meetings, for mustering forces, for propagandizing the unions and peasant groups. 'We will see,' he said grimly, 'which it is: whether the eagle is devouring the serpent, or the serpent is devouring the eagle.'

Night came, and we drove through the blackness of the full sierra — a blackness that thickened in the steep wooded barrancas, where occasionally the lights shone from a lonely cluster of huts. The General could not forgive me that I had timed my trip so that this part of it fell to the night. 'There was so much that I could have shown you if you had gone by day,' he said illogically. 'About Mexico.' I understood what he meant on the return trip, when we went through the mountains by day.

There is much one can learn about Mexico on the trip from Laredo to Mexico City. For it is one thing to be told that in Mexico man faces the two most implacable natural enemies — mountain and drought; and another thing to experience it — to ride hour after hour through the piling mountains, through the dry, merciless up-ended terrain, where there is not a handkerchief of level ground for miles. If corn is planted, it is planted on the steep grades, where one would feel dizzy to stand. And the lonely grass huts cluster perilously on the knife-edge ridges, or in the narrow clefts where the steep valley sides meet. There is not enough rain, even in the rainy season, to unparch the vast dry land; and as one goes north the rainfall is less and less.

One cannot imagine that this land wants humanity, or that life on it could hold any gaiety or charm. It is mostly Otomí land and Otomí life at its most primitive. The Otomís walk along the road, laden with bags of carbon like the burros they drive, and they look at the cars with the uncomprehending stare of animals. The road is not for them. The story is that before it was built President Cárdenas went to the Indians and told them that they would have a road, a splendid highway through the mountains. They thought that was all right, but after the highway came the Indians went to Cárdenas. 'We don't mind the road,' they said, 'but can't you do something about the cars that go over it?' The cars were killing their cattle.

My General kept talking about the highway through the night, with the same enthusiasm he had shown by day. 'Next time,' he told me sternly, 'you must leave Mexico City in the morning. Travel from Mexico City in the morning, from Laredo at night. However, since you are going to stay over in Monterrey...'

But I told him that I did not conform to the idea of staying over in Monterrey.

'I cannot understand that,' he said patiently. 'What it is that you have against me. Haven't we spoken together with confidence?'

Yes, I said, there had been plenty of confianza, that mystic Mexican quality which two people have together, or have not.

'Then I cannot understand it,' he said again. 'What you have against me.' He finally accepted my decision, but he was greatly saddened.

But his gallantry did not desert him. 'When you wish

to sleep, señorita, just indicate it to me,' he said, 'and I will retire to the back of the bus.'

I was obliged to indicate it very soon, for I had already been dozing while he spoke. In the morning when I awoke he was sitting in the back of the bus, looking very wakeful and lonely. 'You slept all through the night,' he reproached me. 'And I did not wake you, even when we crossed the Tropic of Cancer.'

At Monterrey he left us, walking down the street very erect and proud, with his hat jauntily on his head and his military coat on his arm because of the heat. Civilians greeted him with a kind of half-hearted military salute, and he responded in kind. After Monterrey the bus began to act queerly. It started to slow down and to limp as though stricken by paralysis. It went slower and slower, creaking painfully, and at last came to a full stop in front of a fly-blown little lunchroom in the desert that leads to Laredo. The driver turned to us and said gently: 'We will pass some time here.' And as we all piled out he explained further to me (I suppose because I looked puzzled): 'Otherwise they will fine us. The road police will fine us.' 'They will think we have been speeding,' said the other driver. 'That is,' said the first one, 'if we do not lose time here. We will pass them ahead of schedule and they will think we have been speeding.'

Of course they must have been speeding madly all night through the mountains, to be so much ahead of time. But nobody seemed to remember this. So we sat in the lunchroom for an hour, waving the flies away and fanning ourselves in the heat, and then the driver looked at his watch and gave a resounding 'VAMONOS! — Let's go!' and we all went back into the bus again. This time our pace was quite normal, and the road police nodded approvingly when we passed, and the two drivers smiled. They were called Pedro and Pancho, and they were very self-possessed young men, as I discovered on the trip back to Mexico City.

Our bus, this time, was a little more antique than the first one, and a few miles out from Laredo some part of the motor started falling off, and each time that it fell off Pedro and Pancho looked at each other and said pleasantly: 'It fell off again.' One of the passengers thought he could fix the trouble with his toothbrush, and they let him try, but it did not help and the part still kept falling off. It went on all through the night and well into the afternoon of the next day, and it got so that everyone waited for the falling-off act, and piled out docilely when it happened, to stretch and look at the scenery. Only the two Americans got discouraged, and went to sleep in the back of the bus. They had been taking pictures faithfully under the guidance of a young Mexican in a leather jacket, who knew the highway almost as well as my General, and kept telling them when to have their cameras ready. But now they were sound asleep and the Mexican felt worried. 'Awake! Contemplate the beauties of the scenery!' he orated at them, every time the bus stopped. But the Americans slept on, very soundly.

We were near Pachuca when the part fell off and could not be put back again, and we sat on the road wondering how we should get to Mexico City. There was no alarm, for it really never matters to a Mexican if he gets to a place on time or not; and Pedro and Pancho were the calm-

est of all. They kept saying: 'Help will come.' It came in
the form of another bus of the same line, coming toward
us from Mexico City. All the chauffeurs (there were now
four) went into a huddle, and then Pedro and Pancho
turned to us and said: 'We will now all change buses.'
So a change was effected of all the passengers and all the
luggage, and it was very tragic and heartbreaking, for the
luggage got terribly mixed and there were cries and confusion. Then there was some sleight-of-hand with the
motors, and the buses started again. Only *we* were now
going to Mexico City in the bus that had just come from
there; and *they* were going to Laredo in the bus we had
abandoned.

I could not understand the reason for the change, and
I asked Pedro about it when he came to the back seat to
take a nap. 'It is simple,' he said, in that soft indifferent
way in which Mexicans give explanations to fussing Americanos. 'Our bus, as you know, was decomposed. But this
one is even more decomposed, and there is some doubt
that it would ever have reached Laredo, which is quite
far away. So on the whole it was best to change, and take
it back with us. We have divided the motor, but I think
that just the same we will reach Mexico City.'

We did reach it, two hours late, but the greatest good
feeling prevailed that we had reached it at all. And after
that, whenever I would pass the bus terminal in the center
of town, Pedro and Pancho would hail me with a friendly
leer, as comrades who had passed a pleasant time together.
There were no hard feelings, even though we had had a
misunderstanding of the kind that is very likely to occur
between the Latin male and the Anglo-Saxon female. I

had not followed Señor X's advice to cross the bridge and return by the next bus, but decided instead to stay overnight on the Mexican side and make my formal re-entry the next day. Pedro and Pancho said they knew of a hotel where I could stay. In fact it was the hotel where the bus stayed also (in the courtyard) and they would drive me right to it, luggage and all.

On the way I discovered that Pedro and Pancho stayed at the hotel too. We drove to the Serapio Rendon, and they carried my luggage to the desk, and signaled me to make myself ignorant of Spanish, and they bargained with the stout proprietor and got me an excellent room for no more than the ordinary price. 'I have but one regret about this room,' Pancho said ceremoniously, as he put my things in it. 'I regret that it is so far from mine.' It was so delicately put that I could not register the indignation that was in order; but I told them, while I drew forth the tip, that there seemed to have been some misunderstanding. 'Then you don't intend to be my girl for tonight?' Pancho asked bewilderedly, while Pedro eyed me reproachfully. No, I did not. And I tipped them lavishly to reinforce the point. They refused the tips loftily and went away deeply hurt.

I am sure they could not understand the Americana. Most Mexicans have an idea that all American women, because they are free to lead their own lives, are also sexually free; and perhaps those American women who have gone down to Mexico to shed their inhibitions and find romance have aided and abetted this idea. But it is certain that an American woman has to fight for her freedom all over again in Mexico; for Mexican women still live in the nineteenth century, sheltered and domesticated, ruled entirely by the males of the household. I thought of this as I sat outside the Hotel Rendon, looking across the Rio Grande to Texas, and waiting for it to be time to take the bus again. I had crossed the bridge and been in the United States. I had eaten salads and green vegetables in a cafeteria where I could put my elbows on the clean white table. I had walked through Laredo and seen comfortable frame houses and homelike Protestant churches, and it had all been so clean and quiet and orderly and prosperous. I felt very homesick and I wondered if I really wanted to go back to Mexico. And then I knew that if I did not, I should be homesick instead for Mexico, though it is not clean, not orderly and not prosperous. It is difficult or too long to say why this is so, but it is so. The Mexicans say that anyone who has ever been in their country can never forget it, and I am one to believe this.

Pancho came out from the hotel. 'Shall I take your things to the bus, señorita?' he asked with soft courtesy. I said yes, and turned my back on the States and walked toward the bus.

Bitter Bread

OFELIA had studied harder since Manrique's visit, and now she could spell out the headlines in the morning paper. One morning she shook her head disapprovingly. 'Well, it is just as my father said. The millers are going on strike.' I read where she pointed: ANOTHER STRIKE OF THE CORN MILLS.

'We shall be without tortillas,' she said, concerned.

'Then we shall eat bread.'

'I cannot eat bread, señora, it makes me feel quite ill.'

'But you've been eating it all the time!'

'I have felt ill all the time.'

The strike began the next day, and there was no more making of tortillas, for there was no corn dough to be had in all the city. And without the slap-slap sound of tortilla-making, a great silence seemed to have fallen on the streets, and on the huts in the lot too.

The women stood in groups discussing the calamity. The mills had stopped working, the wonderful mills that ground the corn in no time, so that one could go to the tortillerías and buy the dough all prepared, great golden masses of it. Now they would have to grind the corn themselves, kneeling down at the low stone metate; and grind and grind all day, the immemorial servitude of Mexican women.

But Ofelia's mother decided to buy a machine for grinding the corn. That is, if I would advance Ofelia's salary. She had ten pesos put away, and with ten more she could buy a meat-grinder such as the butcher used. Did I think it was a good idea?

I thought it was, and ordered the machine in town, and it came a few days later. Ofelia called me down to witness the unveiling. Señor Escoto squatted on the floor, smilingly aloof from this woman's affair. He would not bother with the machine, but the young aunt put the parts together as deftly as any man, and all the women from the huts came to gaze at it admiringly, and to try turning the handle, which moved with wonderful ease. 'If only Daniel could see it,' Mrs. Escoto sighed. His sweetheart stood in the doorway and looked down the empty sunlit street. 'Yes ... Daniel ...' she said sadly.

But the machine did not work. The grains of corn stuck in it, strong as pebbles, and then no one could turn the handle. And a few days later Ofelia reported sorrowfully: 'We have thrown it away, señora. My father says it is no use, we must give up the hope of eating tortillas until the strike is over.'

So she had spent her pesos for nothing, and she worked silently, looking very unhappy.

'Never mind,' I told her. 'You will make it up quickly. There are so many extra errands to do.'

She nodded. 'It is not the money, señora. It is Daniel. He has disappeared.'

My heart sank, because there had been another robbery in the house, this time at the licenciado's.

'But where has he gone?'

'Pues, that is what we do not know,' she said reasonably. 'We have looked for him all over. My father went to the village where his godfather lives, but no one there has seen him. Nor has he been to the church, nor even to the building where he watches at night. Not one of the peons has news of him.'

'And his sweetheart?'

'She weeps weeps weeps for him all day.'

'Well, he will be back soon. He is young, and it's the most natural thing for a young man to tire of his work and go away for a while.'

'Señora, he is sixteen. And his sweetheart is anxious for the wedding.'

That night I went down to the Germans to go with Ernst to the orchestra. But there was no sound of his viola, and when I came in I saw that he had not gathered his music or folded the music stand. He sat at the table, his hands covering his face.

'Well, tonight they will play without me,' he said heavily, without even the resonance of anger in his voice.

Lutzie signaled to me that he was aufgeregt.

'But we can't,' I said. 'Not the Fiorelle quintet.'

'Ach, the Fiorelle quintet! It was a stupidity to start it, anyway. We are not musicians enough for it. Not those others.'

'But it's not that,' Lutzie told me, and then she lowered her voice. 'Didn't you see it?'

'How could she have seen it?' Ernst asked irritably. 'I tore it out right away.'

'You didn't see it on the mail-box?'

But before I could answer Ernst looked up. His face was haggard. 'It is just like in Germany,' he said, with a listless chant. 'Just like in Germany. We shall have to change our name and move from here.'

'Sh — Ernst! It is not like in Germany.'

'Only small, small.' Suddenly he clenched his fists and trembled with an anger to which all his previous rages had been as nothing. 'I tell you we must fight it!' he shouted. 'We must fight it here, while it is still small.'

'Ernst — please!' And then she told me, giving the news helplessly as if in surrender. 'This morning we found the word Jew written on our letter-box downstairs. Foul Jew. Ernst says the licenciado wrote it.'

'It was his handwriting.'

'Child, you didn't talk to anyone? You didn't tell anyone we are Jewish?'

'No — no one.'

'There, Ernst, you see? You must forgive us, fraülein, we are very much afraid.'

I put my violin down. The music of Schubert's Fiorelle quintet hummed through my mind, but far away and irrelevant, a harmony that would never again be recovered on this earth. Lutzie went for coffee, and Ernst, quiet now, sat drumming his fingers on the table.

'You practiced that first movement too much,' he said severely. But he looked away from me, embarrassed. 'Do you expect to be a soloist, perhaps? I have told you, play the music through. In an orchestra you want rhythm. Rhythm, fraülein!'

'Well, we will have coffee.' Lutzie set the cups down briskly, and began to praise the good coffee that she bought from another German refugee, who peddled it from door to door. And then, as always, the talk turned to the latest robbery.

'I tell you, it was not a genuine robbery,' Lutzie said. 'That licenciado is not in order. He did it himself because he needs the money.'

I made a movement of dissent, but she went on: 'Child, why are you so innocent? Manolo knows. He says the licenciado has not been able to pay his bills — and have you ever known him to work? And that wife of his with her jewels! No, child, those jewels were not stolen. They are hidden away, and the licenciado is lying.'

But at least she did not blame Daniel. 'Daniel has disappeared,' I said.

'Of course,' she agreed calmly. 'Because of all the previous robberies. Do you believe me now? I told you the Escotos were not in order. You will see, Herr Escoto will also disappear.'

Ernst was listening preoccupied. 'It is just like in Germany, all over again. Here, too, we are Jews and must hide. Child!' He put his finger to his lips and peered at me through his glasses. 'You must keep our secret, no? You must not tell anyone — not a soul — that we are Jews and selling our chocolate without permission. Because if it becomes known ...'

'It is bitter bread,' Lutzie sighed. 'Bitter bread.'

So my little paradise collapsed, and as I went upstairs
I felt as if the house were enmeshed in invisible wires, the
cross-currents of hate and suspicion, the war of all against
all.

To beguile Ofelia, who was worried about Daniel's dis-
appearance, we went to the Santa Julia market to buy her
an apron. Santa Julia is a slum where the old adobe houses
are built around corrals noisy with chickens and pigs and
goats, and the unpaved streets are covered with a fine
mixture of mud and refuse and human excrement. But
the way there is pleasant enough. We walked on the em-
bankment of the canal, with the fields on our left stretch-
ing away toward the mountains, and the level white city
below us. The day was clear, and in the east the snow-
topped volcanoes flashed like white lightning in the sky.

The Santa Julia market is as poor as the Merced, but
less crowded, and so the acrobats come there more often.
There is usually a painted clown, hideous and sad; and a
fire-eater, and a little girl in pink tights, and a little boy
who beats the drum. The clown holds out his hat and
moves around through the crowd, shocking the women with
whispered obscenities. The little girl in pink tights raises
a ladder in the air, balances herself a moment, and falls off.
She is dirty and bedraggled, painted like a prostitute. The
fire-eater juggles his flaming torch and puts the burning
end in his mouth. And all the time the drum beats, a
mournful ugly pounding insistent as death, while the Mexicans look on, intent and joyless. Only the flame-swallower
gets a laugh. When he cannot blow out his torch he puts
it between his legs, makes a movement as if passing wind,

and the torch goes out. Then it is over, a few pennies
are tossed into the ring, and the acrobats troop sadly away.
Then there are the little dressed-up dogs who perform
badly or not at all, and the hypnotists and the jugglers,
and the contortionists and the singing beggars — all the
sad perpetual carnival of the market-place.

We were looking at the aprons when the sound of the
drum started, and Ofelia quickly made her choice, and we
rushed over piles of percale and calico and potteries to the
center of the market. This time it was a hypnotist. His
face was really frightening, eaten with leprosy or syphilis
and scarred with smallpox. But he smiled a very white
toothsome smile, and spoke softly to the boy he was
hypnotizing. 'Don't be afraid, nothing can happen.
Don't be afraid...' The boy was holding a little carved
box in his hand. He was staring at the man and he looked
scared to death. 'Now put the box down, put the box
down. Don't be afraid, nothing can happen...' And
he smiled frighteningly and made passes in the air with
long white hands. But the boy could not put the box down.
He lifted it over his head, waved it around, tried to drop
it; but his fingers were paralyzed and would not relinquish
their hold. His face turned pale and he fell to the street,
still holding the box. 'Don't be afraid,' the man said
softly, 'don't be afraid.'

Ofelia tugged at my arm. 'Come away,' she whispered.
'Please come away, señora. The Devil is in the box.'

'Nonsense! The boy is just scared.'

'Please ——' She tugged at my arm. 'Please come
away.' She was as pale as the little boy and her teeth
were chattering.

'Now, Ofelia, you know that boy was only frightened!'
But she could not even listen to me until we were far
away, beyond the sound of the drum.

We were leaving the market when I met Martina. I
knew her from the boarding-house where I had stayed.
She had been a maid there, but she left to go and live with
her handsome sweetheart, Pepe, who was a chauffeur.

'And how is Pepe?' I asked.

Martina lowered her voice. 'Didn't I tell you about
Pepe? Well, he is in jail. He ran over a general's daughter.
Nothing happened to her, but since she was a general's
daughter poor Pepe had to go to jail. Ay, señora, qué
tristeza! He will have to stay there three years unless we
can buy him out. Already he has given them two hundred pesos, but they want more. Ay, señora, all our
savings!'

It made me think about Daniel. If he was in jail, perhaps something could be done for him with money. I had
heard that in Mexico anything can be done with money,
and I was inclined to believe it since this is true of so
many other countries. But of course I was not at all sure
that Daniel was in jail; and yet, as we walked home and
I mulled the facts, I became more and more convinced
of it. Ofelia roused me as we turned away from the canal.
'There's my mother.' I saw Mrs. Escoto's tall figure
ahead of us. It was unusual for her to venture far from
the hut, except to go to the church. 'She went to pray for
Daniel's return, but my father says that prayers will not
help.' I weighed this added evidence. Was Señor Escoto
a skeptic who did not believe in prayer? Or did he know
that Daniel was in jail; and against this overpowering

fact, this hard civic reality — did he feel that prayer was
useless? He might feel that disease and death, fire and
famine, might be averted by prayer. But jail! Now that
was something different! That needed money, and not
prayers. And by the time we reached home I had convinced myself that Daniel was in jail, and I decided to
have it out with Ofelia.

So I asked her: 'Have you, too, gone to church to pray
for Daniel's return?'

'Señora, I went on my knees to the Virgin, and placed
two candles before her. But now — since my father says
praying will not help...'

'And you, Ofelia, what do you make of it?'

'Pues...' She was in deep uncertainty, for the prayers
and candles had never failed her before. Then she sighed.
'My father is always right.'

'And where does he think Daniel is?'

'He doesn't know, he has gone to look for him.
Señora —' She looked at me sideways with fear in her
eyes. 'I want to ask you something. You think Daniel
committed the robbery at the licenciado's! You think
that he's in jail!'

'Oh no...'

'But they are all saying that. All the big mouths on the
lot. And you think so too, señora?'

'I don't know,' I said slowly. 'And even if he were...
Often one does things without thinking, that one regrets
later.'

'Yes,' she agreed angrily. 'Only that did not happen to
Daniel. Certainly that was not the case with Daniel.'

'Then what did happen?'

'Ah ... if we only knew. It is precisely this that we do not know. But now my father is gone too. He has gone to find Daniel, and we have not seen him for two days.'

Lose one thing and it will find something else you have lost, I thought — while Ofelia looked at me, angry and disappointed. So we did not part very well that night, and I knew less and less.

13

Juchitán Wedding

BUT I forgot about the Escotos and their troubles when Alpha's letter came. I had met her in a little bookstore on the Avenue Hidalgo. Señor García who kept the store was small, bald and toothless, but for all that a great student of women. Usually after I had bought the books he recommended (and he was far more useful than all the catalogues in Mexico's disorganized libraries), he would offer me a cigarette and we would smoke while he discussed the question of feminine charm. He found American women very pretty, but basically unattractive. 'They walk badly,' he said, 'and their voices are shrill and they lack repose. But take the women of my tierra. I think they have caught something of the palm trees in their bearing, and when they walk it is like the movement of the wind through

the palms. Wait,' he urged me once, 'I will introduce you
to a woman of my tierra.'

Alpha came in later, and I found her beautiful. Her
face is like a primitive mask, full of austere power. And
she walks superbly. When she was a little girl in her
native Juchitán she went to market barefoot and carrying a basket of fruit on her head. Then she wore the loose
flowing garments of her village, but now even the short ugly
city dress could not disguise the rhythm and grace of her
walk. She walks with head and back very erect, all the
movement in her hips and thighs; and it is something to
watch, like a dance. She had come to Mexico City to
study nursing, and soon after I met her she returned to
her village, to fight against the appalling mortality from
childbirth, against malaria and dysentery and the mysterious pinto that turns the skin blue.

She wrote me to come to Juchitán. She said now was
the time to come because the north wind was blowing,
cooling the tropics, and besides there would be a wedding
in the village which I might want to see. So I bought
quinine and a woven bag to hold my things, and consigned
myself to the ordeal of travel on a second-class train.
Juchitán is a little town on the tropical isthmus of
Tehuantepec, where Mexico narrows between the two
oceans. In space it is not far from the capital, but in
time a slow fifty-two-hour ride on the narrow-gauge National Railway, through heat and jungle. Alpha met me
at the station. She wore the colorful costume of her village
— the full flowered skirt and the loose sleeveless blouse,
bright red and yellow, which bears the Indian name
huipil. She said the Government doctor had come, and

she would have to go to the health station to change into
her uniform. But her cousin was there to drive me to the
house.

'You are from over there?' he asked shyly, when the
car was in motion. It was an old Ford, one of the three
cars in Juchitán.

'From New York,' I specified, for 'over there' means,
vaguely, the United States.

'I understand it is very cold there. I could not live
there because of the cold.'

'That is only in the winter.'

'Yes, that's just it. The question of winter. We are in
winter now, and I find it too cold. This north wind, it
will blow for months.'

It blew relentlessly, herding all the dust of the isthmus
before it. But save for the dust the weather was like the
May of a Northern poet, like the exalted blue days of
wind and brilliant sky that come in the spring after a rain.
In the North such days are rare and must be plucked at
once. But here there was promise of months of them, a
miracle like the month of Sundays.

'Of course in the capital it is often much colder,' Alpha's
cousin continued. 'I am studying in the capital.' He was
very proud. 'But here I spend the vacation.'

Vacation meant to me tennis flannels and sports, and I
asked him what there was to do.

'Do?' he shrugged without understanding. 'Nothing.
I pass the time tranquilly.'

We turned off the road and we were in Juchitán. Mexican towns and villages have a way of impressing themselves in sharp visual images that remain vividly in the

memory like an inner painting, the essential line and color of a place. Thus Monterrey is a wide avenue white with sun, and a dark soaring monument against the hot purple sierra. Taxco is a climb of red-tiled roofs over a hill and the red tiles of the Cathedral dome flashing in the sun. Of Juchitán I remember the flatness and squareness of white adobe houses, the severe line of a white wall joining the sky; and nothing to break the sweep of sky but a solitary palm, lifting shaggy fronds on a curving trunk. And always the wind driving veils of dust through the unpaved streets, and the women walking in the wind and the dust, their skirts blowing.

Alpha's aunts came out to welcome me. In the big white-walled living-room they brought atole to drink, and water in an earthen jar, talking among themselves in Zapotecan but with Spanish for me. They spread a fresh sheet on the bed, and then, shyly smiling, they withdrew and left me alone to sleep. When I awoke, a little girl was standing in the doorway and staring at me. She fled when I moved, leaving the door ajar, and I looked out at the shaded back portico with its two massive Spanish pillars framing the stone-paved patio. The women were working, carrying gourds with water across the patio — a slow stately parade as if they had all eternity for doing things, and time did not matter. Nor does time matter in Juchitán. It may be because of the wind eternally blowing, making a vast monotony of sound out of day and night, so that one does not notice the treacherous hours slipping away; or perhaps it's because all the things that make time are lacking. Where there are factory whistles, crowds, trains, real estate developments, spring millinery

sales and winter clothes to put away, one must live with
an eye on the clock and the calendar. But in Juchitán
there is only the wind and the dust, rumbling ox-carts
and a sleepy river, the ancient pageantry of the market-
place, days eternally the same.

I watched the slow motion of the women until I dozed
off again, and when I awoke the door was closed and the
room dark. It was the main living-room of the house, but
in complete disorder. Carved chests and bolts of cloth and
pottery piled helter-skelter, a confusion of furniture from
which one picked out an altar with a figure of the Virgin,
a dressing-table laden with Pond's cold cream and powder,
a sewing machine. Two hammocks strung across the width
of the room cleared the disorder like boats over the waves.
They were for sleeping in the hot weather, but no one had
thought to remove them now that they were not needed.
But perhaps this confusion too reflected the Juchitán idea.
For order represents our fear and nervousness. We create
ordered interiors as a protest over the passing of things,
to define our mortal lives against the void of time. Yet
where no one is worried about time and mortality, why
bother with ordered interiors?

The door opened and Alpha's Aunt Electra came in.
I had noticed her before because, unlike the other women,
she had green eyes, and except for her dark skin she looked
so much like an aunt of mine that I had trouble not to
call her by that aunt's name. She had changed her every-
day red and yellow huipil for one splendidly embroidered
in black and gold, and instead of her plain black skirt
she wore a red embroidered one, with the ceremonial white
pleated ruffle at the bottom. In the morning she had gone

barefoot, but now she put on high-heeled shoes. Then, seated at the dressing-table, she began to smear her face with the Pond's cold cream, as expertly as any débutante who has endorsed the product. 'For the dust,' she said. 'Don't you want some?' She seemed puzzled when I said no.

'But you are coming with us?'

She told me about the wedding in the village. There would be four dances, all out-of-doors, the first at the home of the bride's godmother. Already the men had gone to help build the canopy of branches for the dance, and the women were making ready for a visit to the godmother. The girl who was getting married belonged to the well-to-do class, and the wedding festivities would absorb all the village, at least all the families that lived in the stone and adobe houses, but not those that lived in the grass huts near the river. These are the poor of Juchitán. They might trail the wedding procession through the streets, and stand looking in on the dances, but they could not be counted as wedding guests.

'Yes, of course I am coming,' I said, and Electra nodded, pleased, and gave me a handkerchief with eggs tied in it. All the women carried eggs tied in a handkerchief, and we went out together into the dusty street.

In the godmother's house the women who had come before us sat against the wall, a fresco of bright huipils, flowing skirts sculptured at the bottom with stiff white ruffles, dark faces framed in wreathed braids. The godmother was old as an ancient deity. She sat on the floor sifting flour. There was a metate for grinding corn, and each woman in turn rose and knelt at the metate and ground some of the corn grains. From outside where the men were building the canopy came bursts of laughter. First the voice of one man speaking, and then the ribald burst of laughter. But the women worked in grave silence, as if the event they were preparing were not a marriage but had to do with death. Each guest on entering gave eggs to the godmother, and dropped a coin into a gourd on the floor. I had no change and put in a peso. The old woman looked at it, consulted in Zapotecan with another old woman, and then carefully counted out nine coins from the gourd. She was making change of the peso and she brought it to me and said gravely: 'Each one gives only ten centavos.' And I could not tell whether I was being rebuked for vainglorious display, or because I had broken the custom. Then we had sweet biscuits and atole flavored with cinnamon and chocolate, and everyone received a cigarette wrapped in paper. Not to be wrong again, I put mine behind my ear when I saw all the other women doing that.

After a while Electra looked at me. 'Do we go?' she asked.

'As you wish.'

'We go, then?'

'When you are ready.'

But she rose and I followed her out, and we walked toward the plaza while I wondered if I had committed a breach of etiquette in leaving so soon. But at any rate I still had my cigarette behind my ear, as Electra had hers, and I would not touch it until she touched hers.

'Our life is very different from yours,' Electra said, courteously making conversation.

'Different, but more interesting.'

'Ah, you think so?' Her green eyes were opaquely polite. 'I think you must laugh at us here.'

'No, I am sorry if you think so.'

She was silent, walking supplely in her high-heeled shoes. I had thought she was tall, but walking beside her I found I was the taller. It is the flowing dress and splendid walk of the Juchitán women that gives an illusion of tallness.

'I have been to the capital,' Electra said. 'There it is very different from here. They laughed at me there. I went dressed just as I do here, and the boys ran after me on the street and called: "Hungarian!" Is it true that the Hungarians dress as we do?'

'There is great similarity.'

'Then they, too, are of Tehuantepec?'

'No, they are of Europe.'

'How rare,' she mused, 'that they are not of Tehuantepec and should dress the same. Still, I did not like being laughed at. The capital is very wonderful, but I could not live there. They laugh at us and they do not speak Zapotecan.'

'But you speak Spanish too.'

'Apenas,' she said. 'Hardly. I believe you speak more of Spanish than I do.'

'Oh no.'

'Certainly. We are taught Spanish in school, but Zapotecan is our language.'

'But you see how useful Spanish is, for we can understand each other.'

'Really?' Her eyes gave no hint of mockery, but I was not sure. 'Over there' — she pointed across an empty

lot that looked as though it were in the slow process of being turned into a playground — 'is the church.'

It stood behind a rusted iron gate, a very plain medieval-
looking mass of stone, bespeaking the earliest period of the
Spanish church-builders. Perhaps the work of the Fran-
ciscan friars who did not have much time for building
churches while they converted Indian souls by the thousands.

'It is always kept closed,' Electra said rather sadly, 'and
there is no priest. But tomorrow one is coming from
Tehuantepec to marry the betrothed couple. That will
be done in the chapel, which is always kept closed too, but
tomorrow the priest will open it.'

We came to the plaza and sat down near the bust of
Júarez. There are two statues that haunt Mexico. One is
the statue of Cuatemoc, the Aztec prince who defied the
Spaniards. He stands on the Reforma in his Indian mantle
and plumed headdress, with his long spear raised for hurl-
ing; and replicas of him are likely to appear anywhere.
The other is the statue of Júarez, an Indian too, and the
great national hero of modern Mexico. Cuatemoc crops
up all over in little souvenir copies, much like our Statue
of Liberty. Júarez has the plazas. This one happened to
be a very bad machine-made bust. I had expected something better, for Júarez was of the same blood as the
people of Juchitán. The plaza was deserted, flecked with
sun and shade on the white benches and on the bandstand
in the center.

'There is never any music,' Electra said, continuing her
sad record of things abandoned. But it was only Spain
that was abandoned — the closed church, the disused

plaza. The life of Juchitán is still Indian, and the marriage of the bridal pair in the chapel would be the merest incident in the long pagan wedding ceremonies, ceremonies so old that their meaning is forgotten, or only told obscurely on the lips of some ancient of the village.

'Are you anxious to see the bride?' Electra asked.

'I am very curious.'

'To me she is not pretty,' Electra said disdainfully. 'But she is marrying very well. Her husband is rich and they will go to live in the capital, where he teaches. I would not like that, living in the capital.'

'But if your husband wished it?'

'Pues ... I have no husband.'

'But when you have one ...'

She was silent a moment. 'I do not think I will ever have one.'

'But you are young and pretty.'

'Oh no, I am old. The question is over for me.'

'I think you will marry very soon.'

'No, I think it will not be.'

She shook her head and I wondered what had happened to her. Perhaps she was disappointed in love, or perhaps there had never been a mate for her in Juchitán. They say that the women of Juchitán outnumber the men. Or it may have been some strangeness in herself, something for a psychiatrist to unravel. For there is no climate in the world where the human heart will not go awry. But whatever it was, she had become one of that sad sisterhood scattered over the world — a maiden aunt. Poor Electra! The Mexicans say of a spinster that 'she stayed to dress the saints.' But here the church was closed, and

there were not even the pale waxen figures of the saints
to dress. She was looking out over the plaza, where the
wind whirled dust around the forsaken bandstand.

'It is sad here,' she said, 'I do not know what it is, but
sometimes I feel a great sadness.'

When we returned to the house, Alpha was there with
Andrés, her sweetheart, and Chavo; and we sat down to
a meal of turtles' eggs and goat meat, served by Electra.
All the women but Alpha ate in the big smoky barn in
back of the patio.

I had met Andrés in Mexico City, and from the first
he had treated me with affable mockery.

'She comes from the United States,' he said, introducing
me to Chavo. 'A country strong but stupid.'

'I have been to your country,' Chavo said in English.
'I have been there before I have come to Mexico. I have
learned English there.'

'She comes from New York,' Andrés said. 'They do
not speak much English there.'

'I have been in New York,' Chavo continued. 'It is
wonderful. So many skycrappers.'

'She does not understand you.'

'And I have learned a song of your country — "O
Columbia the Gin of the Ocean."'

'Gem,' I said.

'Gin,' he insisted. 'That is how I have learned it.' They
both sang it with their hands to their hearts.

Chavo was a refugee from Spain. His wife and child
were still in a concentration camp in France and he had
not heard from them for many months. He took out a

picture and showed it to me. 'I have never seen the boy,' he said, 'because he was born after I came to Mexico. But he looks like me, doesn't he? All he needs is the mustache.' ·

Andrés, too, had fought in Spain, and the talk of the Spanish civil war continued late into the afternoon, the distant clamor of arms through the wind of Juchitán. Then we heard the first imperious notes of the marimba, carried on the wind. The wedding dance had begun.

Strictly speaking, there were not four wedding dances, but rather a continuous state of dancing, a sort of common village responsibility not to let the dance die down. So that people went home to sleep only for a few hours, and then were up again to take over from those who had not yet slept. And day and night the women put on their best huipils and long ruffled skirts, and their ornaments of shining Yankee coins; and day and night the wind carried the sound of the marimba tirelessly beating out slow Cuban danzones, until it seemed like the sound of the wind itself.

The first dance began with staid formalities. The women sat with downcast eyes, their aloof modesty belying the provocation of their bright huipils and tinkling gold ornaments. The men stood apart, talking, with only an occasional glance for the women. Night had come, and the flaring torches threw a painted green light on the leafy canopy and bronze shadows on the faces of the marimba players, studiously beating the instrument in a corner. 'One dances only with those one knows,' Alpha said. She had twined red ribbons in her hair, and her earrings gleamed under the dark braids. All the women, even the wrinkled old ones who had come only to gossip, were resplendent in their native dress. But the dressing-up of the men had brought them to a sad drabness. They looked awkward in their city clothes, not mated to the pagan splendor of the women. Andrés and Alpha were the first to dance, a languorous two-step; and as each couple joined, the young bloods gathered outside raised a derisive shout. Unseen but heard, like ribald birds haunting the canopy, they improvised couplets about the dancers. Everyone stopped dancing and listened when the couplet promised to be especially spicy. There was a couplet for Chavo and me, of which I caught only the word gringa, for the rest was in Zapotecan. And Andrés would not translate or tell me why everyone had laughed.

Later came the Sandunga. It is the dance of the isthmus, and it began with a stir of expectancy, a flourish on the marimba, and the word 'Sandunga' like a warning and a call from mouth to mouth. First the women danced alone, a quiet polka step, demurely holding their skirts. The men joined slowly, shuffling around their partners, with their hands behind their backs. Save for the unvarying step, the holding of the skirts, and the posture of the men, the figures are informal and the dancers move freely as they will, self-absorbed, though always oriented toward their partners. Courtship and indifference, pursuit and retreat, chastely stylized; while only the anguished cry, 'Ay, Sandunga!' carries the inner tension.

Chavo and I did not dance the Sandunga, for without the mood of inner absorption, which is not to be learned, one cannot dance it. We sat watching and listening to the eloquent comments of Andrés's uncle. An old fellow

with a melancholy Indian face, he had attached himself
to us like a one-man Chamber of Commerce, to see that
we stayed in a constant glow of appreciation. 'The things
of Juchitán!' he cried, beating his breast with one hand
while a gesture of the other encompassed the dancers.
'The things that are very much ours! Observe, O strangers,
the quaint customs of my people. Go forth and publish
them to the world.' Later, when the Sandunga was over
and everyone went out to take refreshments under the
sky where the stars seem so strangely low, he cornered us
and began to talk about Júarez, whom he called 'the
exquisite Indian.'

'I see him in the hills of Oaxaca, a simple shepherd lad
feeding his flock, unaware of the great destiny that awaits
him.' The narrative lengthened, the gestures grew more
dramatic, and people gathered around him.

We danced that night until the wind of morning began,
and then, after a few hours' sleep haunted by the sound
of the marimba, we followed the wedding procession
through the wind and the dust to the ancient chapel where
the priest who had come from Tehuantepec performed the
marriage rite. And we danced all of that day and again
the next morning, when all the women came with colored
pinwheels and loaves of corn bread that they gave to the
bride. But at night the bride and groom left the dance,
and everyone looked toward the bride's home, waiting for
the fireworks which would show that the bride was a
virgin.

Mariana who was selling refreshments told us about it.

'Now it is over,' she said, 'there will be only one more
dance tomorrow, for the old men and the old women, when

they will get drunk and tear their clothes and scream, not knowing what they are doing. But now it is over for the bridal pair, all but the proving. How sad the bride will be tonight, how she will cry.'

'And if there are no fireworks?' Chavo asked.

'Then, señor, it will mean she was not a virgin. Then her husband will torture her. He will beat her and ask: Who was it? Who was it? He will beat her until she confesses, and then he will return her to her mother.'

'How, if they are already married . . .'

'Even so, señor. But possibly he may choose to keep her, only it will be very bad for her. He will torture her all the time and make her very miserable. However,' she added with a shrug of contempt, 'I believe she will be a virgin. These rich ones, they save themselves. She will be a virgin, but she will cry just the same.'

We asked why the bride would cry just the same.

'Because it will be the first time,' Mariana said, 'and she will suffer very much.'

Andrés's uncle was very drunk that night. He began to beat his breast for his mestizo blood. 'Look at me,' he said abjectly, 'I am not pure Indian! My blood has been adulterated with the blood of the conquerors. That is my great sorrow. Yes, I must confess, I am not pure Indian. I am the degenerate son of a once proud race.' He became more and more abject, pointed to himself as one whose life had been miscast in a backward little pueblo, and said the only thing he could be proud of in a misspent life was that he had given Andrés wings to fly from Juchitán. 'Wings!' he cried, flailing his arms and eyeing us fiercely. 'Wings to fly from this wretched little village.' His daughter finally came and dragged him away, and he had time only for a last wave of the hand while he exhorted us: 'Go forth, O strangers, sing my race, sing my people!'

Chavo obeyed him that very night by learning a song in Zapotecan, after the fireworks had come and nearly everyone had gone home, and only a few couples remained, dancing over the ground strewn with confetti. He had wanted a piano, but failing that, he took charge of the marimba and played the songs of the Spanish civil war on it. And then one of the musicians taught him a love-song of Juchitán. 'The corn and beans are ripe in my field, for you my beloved ...' But Chavo learned the words in Zapotecan. The next morning he sang them in the market-place, while we were having refrescos, to a crowd of open-mouthed listeners. I can still remember the delighted, hypnotized smile on the face of one of the little boys when he heard his own speech coming so strangely from alien lips — that which must be a fairly pleasurable experience for the first time, and for a young provincial the beginning of wisdom that there are other worlds beyond his own.

The market-place of Juchitán, as in all Tehuantepec, is kept entirely by the women, while the men are relegated to the inferior work of the fields. And whenever we went through the market it was a holiday for the women. They would have it that Chavo and I were brother and sister, because, 'Look you! they are both blond.' And because of our strange blondness we were treated with awe, but also with contempt — like conquering heroes who could only honor them by deigning to buy, but also like prisoners of war who must run a gantlet of uncomplimentary remarks. Especially about Chavo's hair, which is very curly. Andrés translated for us: It was like a rat's nest. It was like a fence covered with brambles, like a leafy arbor, like the way out of a mountain.

Mariana kept a stand under the portico, and whenever we came she greeted us with: 'What does your heart say?' Our hearts usually said spicy tostadas, and while we ate she told us about her man who was away working on the roadbuilding, and how she would not marry him because then he would begin to boss her. 'It is only for the rich,' she said, 'marriage!' She was good-looking like all the women of Juchitán, but very short and plump, and when she spoke she looked thoughtfully at Chavo.

We went to the last dance, and watched the drunken antics of the old people. They danced over their vomit, smirking and mimicking the graces of the young. The marimba beat out a tom-tom, and they began to cavort around, crouching, almost on all fours, a dance from the ancient past that needed masks and animal heads. Mariana was there, very drunk and undone, and she came over and asked Chavo to dance with her. When he hesitated she burst into tears. 'You despise me!' she said, looking up at the six feet of Chavo and his hair shining in the sun. 'You really despise me!' He danced with her.

It was the last of the wedding festivities, and at night only the sound of the wind blew through the plaza. Outside the cantina that cast the only light in the windy darkness, we sat drinking beer with the village celebrities — the poet who wrote the song Chavo learned, and Andrés's uncle who teaches in the school, and the deputy to the National Congress. The deputy, a burly fellow with a back-slapping manner learned in the capital, threw his leg over his bench as though he were mounting horse-back. He was dressed like a campesino and two splendid pistols gleamed in his belt.

'He is a politician,' Andrés told me, sotto voce. 'Not the best we can do, but he is in favor of schools.'

The talk was of asking the Government for another school in Juchitán, and of starting a newspaper in Zapo-tecan. Mexico's Indian groups speak over fifty languages and dialects, and thus far the movement has been to impose Spanish on these groups, as a unifying thread in the patchwork of speeches. All the schools have been conducted in Spanish, and the Indian pupils, who have never known a written language of their own, have had the double burden of learning to read and write in a foreign tongue. The results have not been good, for lan-guage is the very breath of the inner life. Deprived of their own speech, the Indians have lost contact with their own culture and traditions, and their habitual forms of thought and feeling. And Mexico still remains a country in which nearly half the population is illiterate.

But now there is a new movement to conduct education in the indigenous languages. Education, pamphlets, news-papers, and books in the language of each pueblo, with Spanish coming later as the life of the pueblo changes and grows modern. The leaders of this movement are wise, but no wiser than the missionaries who came after the conquest, and set themselves to learning the native tongues for purposes of conversion. Only now the purpose is to create the Mexican nation, unified and modern. So Andrés, who teaches at the National University, talked about a newspaper in Zapotecan, while the deputy listened, his large sunburned hands resting on the table. Meanwhile Alpha's cousin had gone for his guitar, and routed out the best guitar-player in Juchitán, and the two of them came back, already thoughtfully plucking their instruments. Silence fell on the talk as they began 'La Llorona,' the love-song that is sung all over the isthmus.

'You were coming from the church, Llorona, when I first saw you, in a huipil so splendid that I thought you were the Virgin.' The melody begins with a high querulous phrase, falls in a slow twisting scale reluctantly downward to the last held note. Then again the high-pitched beginning, complaint and reproach, and the slow downward twisting, the song caught in an endless spiral of yearning and anguish and despair. 'Ay, Llorona, Llorona of the heights! I am like the mule-driver who comes to the cold height to build him a fire.'

There must be a score of known stanzas, but the singers improvise more. Andrés took the guitar, thrummed a moment, and began: 'Where you tread, Llorona, on the shore of the sea, where you tread on the shore of the sea, the waves bring pearls to the sand ... Ay, Llorona, Llorona of the infinite waves ...' This poetic exaggeration is greatly appreciated, but the circle of listeners who had gathered around us gave no sign. The market was deserted and the women had gone home, but the men stood listening with folded arms, relaxed and impassive. And the lighted clock in the market-place showed twelve before the song of Llorona was over, and the guitars rested on the table, and the listeners melted away as silently as they had gathered, their white trousers gleaming in the dark.

The next morning we took the bus to Tehuantepec, the town from which the isthmus receives its name. We waved good-bye to the women in the market-place as the bus pulled out, but their last shouted remarks were lost because we were busy pulling down the canvas against the dust. All through the ride over a road that pushed the jungle away on both sides, the dust was like an enemy pursuing us, and when the bus stopped the dust caught up and boarded it; but the women never covered the piles of tortillas that took up all the floor space. Humanity and freight travel together on the isthmus, where for the most part the roads are easier for travel by burro than by any wheeled vehicle. Andrés had said it was easier for those of Juchitán to go to Mexico City than to Oaxaca, capital of the state and not two hundred miles away.

The norther died down in Tehuantepec, and the air felt baked, and we went to the river where we lay down on the damp sand and argued about the women of Juchitán. Andrés said they were probably happier than the women of my country. I thought of the huge barn in back of the patio, where the women cooked on an open fire, stooping to the flames in the dark smoky air; and of how they walked back and forth across the patio, carrying a little water each time in a gourd — a stately and picturesque procession with their white ruffles sweeping the dust, but also a treadmill of unnecessary steps. And I said that at any rate the women of my country would be more efficient, and devise some system of running water, and so have time for something else. 'For what?' Andrés asked contemptuously. 'For dressing themselves and reading stupid books!' He had been in the United States and felt he could talk with authority.

The sun went down and the bathers left the river and a last ox-cart crossed it, rumbling noisily on the opposite bank, and then there was silence broken only by the distant cry of children and the far-off whistling of the train. The railroad tracks run through all the length of Tehuantepec, close against the white mud houses, so that it has something of the air of a poor suburb in an industrial American city. Once Tehuantepec was the center of all the commerce of the isthmus, but now that commerce is a thing of the past, and there is only one train a day which may appear at any time between noon and midnight. We heard it whistling nearer now, and Chavo stirred and looked out over the river. 'This is the way we used to lie in the concentration camp,' he said, 'without food, without shelter, in the winter in France.' It grew dark and the mosquitoes began to bite, and we got up flailing our arms and went back to take the bus to Juchitán. It was my last night there. The next day we went to Salina Cruz to have a look at the Pacific, and from there I would go directly back to Mexico City.

Dust and jungle again, and the organ cactus lifting huge stiff fingers against the sky, and then a bend of the road whirling the sea into view. Salina Cruz is a deserted port, bewitched and spellbound, with a spell cast on it by history and the fate of nations. It has declined with all the isthmus, and the Panama Canal now draws the traffic that used to come to the isthmus ports. We walked to the end of the breakwater and looked back to the scattered white houses of the town, asleep between the sea and the low sierras that have ended their march to the sea. There was no sound, only the wind and the sea, silence and doom on everything else. On the wharves the lighterage cranes hung motionless over the rotting boards, a few rusting freight cars stood empty on the tracks. The little boy who showed us a place where we might bathe without danger from sharks said that a ship might be expected in a few months. Perhaps, he said.

We sent him ahead to order lunch at the hotel, and meanwhile we climbed the cliff to the lighthouse. The lighthouse keeper felt called on to justify his office. 'There will be boats,' he said, shaking his head at the Pacific as though it were a recalcitrant child, 'when the harbor is dredged. Now they cannot enter because of the sand.'

He invited us to share his tortillas, but we went back to the hotel which was justly advertised as 'the most ventilated in Salina Cruz.' For the wind blew like a gale through the empty corridors, and through the big dining-room and bar where there was never the merrymaking of sailors any more. The landlady's little girl served us with world-weary poise. She said she was going away to a school in Mexico City soon, and very glad of it, for it was a fine thing to be leaving Salina Cruz. 'There is nothing to do here,' she said. 'The movies come only once a week.' 'But bathing?' She sighed as one who is denied even the simplest pleasures. 'The norther blows too strong, and besides, there are sharks.' She mentioned them with dainty disdain, as one might mention the buzzing of a fly. 'Do you know Shirley Temple?' she asked me, and I said yes, I had seen her in the movies. 'But you don't know her personally?' 'No, unfortunately not.' She looked at me from the door with severe disapproval. There was a wedding in Salina Cruz too. In the

big hall of the hotel the women were twisting white papers
into long streamers and hanging them from the ceiling.
There would be a wedding dance under the streamers,
but just one dance. Salina Cruz does not follow the customs of Juchitán, for the sea has weaned it from the rest
of the isthmus.

And brought strange fish to it. At night in the tiny
cantina near the docks we met a tall lanky Scotchman,
and a cockney-speaking Englishman. Andrés looked at
them and said with malicious joy: 'Speak to them in
English. See if they understand you.' And the look on
the face of the Scotchman when I addressed him in
English was pure ecstasy. We all sat down and the Scotchman pledged us in Spanish and Gaelic and ordered a
carton of beer to be sent to his house, where we were to
go afterward to meet his wife. She was a native girl
named Teresina, but the Scotchman called her Terry.
He was terribly afraid that we would disapprove of his
having married her, but he said he couldn't help it, because
she was beautiful and he loved her, and he would lay
down his life for her, or at least spend the rest of it in
Salina Cruz just to be near her. We said we thought it
was O.K., and Andrés drank, 'To the triumph of the
mongrel!' The Englishman also was married to a native
girl, but he was rather morose about it and silent. When
he did speak, in a thick cockney brogue, I could not
understand him. Andrés and Chavo looked at each other
as much as to say: 'You see? She doesn't really know
the king's English.'

Terry came in, and she was beautiful. She sat by smiling
while the Scotchman told us how he wanted to leave

Salina Cruz because there was no more work there. An American company had been dredging the harbor, but it was being replaced by a Mexican company. He might work with this company, but he didn't like working for Mexicans. So he wanted to go away from Salina Cruz, but he was afraid to travel with Terry, because in some place like Vera Cruz she would surely go off with another man. A younger man. We asked Terry about it and she said no, but we didn't feel sure. She had a baby with her, a very dark thin little thing, but it turned out that it was not hers and the Scotchman's. It seems they could not have a baby, and he asked us whether we thought it was because he was Scotch and Terry Indian. But anyway they had a dog with a wonderful name. He went outside and called it. 'Caralampio!'

I was worried about the train, but the Scotchman insisted that we go to his house. There Chavo banged the piano while the Englishman sang 'Rule, Britannia,' and the Scotchman did contortions, flinging his leg over his shoulder. On the wall there were big lithographs of the ships of the British navy, looking very becalmed and unmaritime. And when we left and walked across the plaza to the station, the town too seemed no more than a lithograph in the moonlight, so still and unreal it was, with only the norther blowing a gale from the land. And blowing all night, while the train creaked slowly through the sierras, away from the forgotten towns of the isthmus to the high central plateau of Mexico.

The Little White Bird

THE RAINS stopped and in their stead came the dust; walls of yellow dust moving in from the barren mountains to the north, as if these had changed their essence and were on the march. In the early afternoons the streets were dark as twilight, and one tasted dust and breathed it, and almost touched it in the air. People shook their heads over the rains. There was fear for the crops. 'The waters have ceased too early,' everyone said. The valley needed rain, and instead it was being smothered in a dry death.

But the dust-storms stopped too, and there came a morning of yellow sky and a stillness in the air, and then a movement of wind and a sound of thunder in the mountains. It grew cold in the afternoon and the sky filled with clouds, low and opaque, weirdly purple. The hailstorm broke soon after. The drops were as big as pebbles and came slanting against the window, rebounding with the fury of their fall and with a sound as of thousands of drums. In the lot there were faint cries, the women calling to the children, and then nothing but the whiteness and fury of the hail. When it was over the sky shone with a polished deep blue and a radiant sun. But the ground was still white with hail and the air as cold as night.

Ofelia and her little sister came up, very excited. 'Ay, what a storm! Holy heart! The whole house is drenched and there is hail on the floor and on the bed.'

They were barefoot, wet and shivering. 'Put on shoes,' I said, 'and keep out of the wet.' But they went on about the storm.

'Aunt Delfina was caught in the street. She came in nearly beaten to death. But all the rest of us were in the house, and my mother said we should pray, and we fell on our knees and prayed, and with that the storm went away. Ay, what a storm. Sacred heart!'

The children of the lot played in the hail, running over it with bare feet, shrieking with the coldness of it. But that night Ofelia and her little sister were sick. They sat on the bed, bright-eyed and rosy, but quiet as if speech had been stricken from them. I said they should be put to bed, but Mrs. Escoto shrugged. 'Pues ... the bed is soaked through, señora, and besides, it is nothing. It is very natural after the cold and the hail.'

'It will pass,' Aunt Delfina said. 'Tomorrow they will be all right.'

In the morning the two of them lay on the bed, still rosy-looking as if in the first flush of slumber. But their foreheads were burning and Ofelia did not open her eyes when I spoke to her. The women were frightened now — not because the children were sick, but because they had surrendered to their sickness. They were frightened by their lying down, this pantomime of death. 'Let them get up and move around,' Aunt Delfina said complainingly. 'Then they'll be all right.' And Mrs. Escoto nodded. For as long as one moved around, all was well. The appearance of life and health was a strong enough magic to make any sickness go away. But once one lay down and surrendered — that was a magic that invited death.

I persuaded them to stuff the drafty holes in the wall with paper and to put dry covering on the bed. Mrs. Escoto gathered the straw sleeping mats. They had been sunned in the morning and they were the only things in the house that were dry. Later Lutzie came with tea and pills and a thermometer. 'You measure the fever with this,' she said, and told them how to use it. The women handed the thermometer from one to another with respectful acquiescence. But they had not used it when I came back in the afternoon. 'It is very hard to use,' Mrs. Escoto said. 'I have no head for numbers.' It was raining again and the hut was chilly and damp, smelling of the charcoal fire in the next room, that gave smoke but no warmth. The women sat on packing-cases with their arms folded over the ends of their rebozos. They thanked me effusively for coming, but begged me not to come again. 'So much bother for you,' Mrs. Escoto said, rocking herself gently. 'So much bother for nothing.' Because all this fuss was dangerous, a bad magic certain to attract the lurking death. And above all, to call a doctor! 'No,' Mrs.

Escoto said firmly, 'it is not necessary, señora. Not necessary by any means.'

But that night we sat in the hut waiting for Doctor González. 'That Lupita!' Mrs. Escoto said. 'She is babbling about the chickens that died. But Ofelia, she cries out that she is afraid. Who knows of what she babbles?' But I thought I knew, or could guess. Was it Manrique?

He was pursuing her, flying over the tree-tops of the Reforma, large and black as a monstrous crow . . . and waving his arms, and the light was flashing like lightning on his glasses, and she ran before him looking up and screaming because her legs would not move, and at any moment she must fall. *You must go to school, Ofelia, you must go to school.* Mortal sin, mortal sin! O father, I have sinned! I confessed and did not wash my mouth afterward. O father, because the devil was in the box and he winked at me, and I took him in my arms, small as a bird against the breast, and I kissed him, father, and did not wash my mouth. *You must go to school, Ofelia, you must go to school.* In my apron? It's not an apron, fool, can't you see it's a shroud and you are dead? The mordelon killed you. He took you down down into the earth, deeper than the heart of the volcanoes, and did it to you there, and you are dead under the earth, dead and my feet cannot move, and the devil dances over me like a little bird. *Don't be afraid, don't be afraid, nothing can happen . . .* Come away, señora, come away, because the earth is crumbling and piling on top of me and the devil is in my mouth like a live coal. O father, let me close my mouth, give me the wafer, I am burning — deep deep under the earth where there is a sound of thunder. *You must go to school, Ofelia, you must go to school.* He took off his glasses and hurled them to the earth and two burning candles sprang from them in front of the altar. They grew large as white pillars, but whirling with flames, and the Virgin stood between them with a terrible mask on her face, and the devil flew out from her breasts like a little bird, in the form of a little white bird. *Quick, quick . . . the wafer, father.* Her arms flailed in the air trying to catch it, but it danced like a feather in the wind and she was flying over the tree-tops with her arms reaching out for it, trying to catch it. But it spread its wings and grew monstrous as the face of the earth, and danced over her where she lay, deep under the earth in a whirling darkness. *The mordelon did it to you, the mordelon!* And his name was Edouardo. Ed-ou-ardo.

But the apron did not cover her, and she was walking through the market dying of shame because the apron did not cover her, and the hypnotist smiled and said: 'Put it down, put the box down.'

'But I can't, I can't.'

'Of course you can, it is easy.'

'I am looking for Edouardo.'

'He is in the box. He's a little bird.'

'He has my apron.'

And Edouardo came toward her, smiling, with a bag of crackers in his hand. 'There's an extra cracker,' he said, 'tell the señora.' And then the hypnotist took her hand and they were walking along the canal, and she was dying of shame because her apron did not cover her. She was going to school with the box in her hand, and they came to her house where Daniel was lying dead, only he was very small, and her mother lifted him up and put him away and said: 'Tomorrow is his wedding.' Then she opened her book and wrote her name and she was in school, and Manrique said: 'You must go to school, Ofelia, you must go to school.' Then Daniel began to cry like a baby, and her mother lifted him up and gave him to the priest, who put the wafer on his forehead, and Daniel began to move and Manrique said, 'Now he is not dead any more.' She was still in the hut yet she was in school, and Manrique said: 'The señora wants you to sweep with this,' and he gave her a pencil covered with tooth-marks. 'That's because everyone goes to school,' he said. She went on writing faster and faster with wonderful skill, and there was a strange light all around her and she was exceedingly happy, and then she began to sweep with the pencil Manrique gave her. But it grew bigger and bigger in her hands until she could not hold it any more, but she could not put it down either, her fingers stuck to it. *'Don't be afraid,'* said the hypnotist, *'don't be afraid.'* But the pencil kept growing, taller than the candles in front of the Virgin, and it flamed like a candle and grew monstrous and unending, and she fell in a faint before it, plummeting down into whirling blackness. *Mortal sin, mortal sin!* O father, I have sinned, give me the wafer because I am thirsty, because the devil is in my mouth like a live coal.

Come away, señora, come away, because the devil is in the box and he flies like a bird, and he is under the hands of the Virgin between her breasts, moving to be free, and he dances over me lightly as a bird, but I cannot move, I cannot touch him. Come away, I am afraid, I am afraid. But the hypnotist smiled, waving his hands in the air.

'Don't be afraid, don't be afraid, nothing can happen.' But the mordelon was going too fast and she could not keep up with him, and she ran after him and she called, Edouardo, Edouardo. And then she was not afraid, but stepped on to the motor-cycle and held his waist, and they went very fast down the Reforma, faster than the wind. And the motor-cycle lifted into the air and flew like a bird, and everyone stood on the Reforma looking up, and she was ashamed ashamed. And she begged Edouardo to stop, but he was holding her and they were flying together, flying strangely together, and he was holding her, but deep under the earth, deeper than the heart of the volcanoes. And she could not move, she was dead with her apron around her like a shroud, winding and winding, endlessly winding . . .

'It is fifty centavos,' the woman said, and she began to cut the apron from the bolt of cloth.

'That's enough,' the señora said, 'that's enough.'

But the apron kept unwinding itself, unwinding unwinding, and she could not stop it and she screamed because it was a shroud.

Come away, señora, come away. 'Yes, we are going to school,' the señora said. But the hypnotist smiled and said, 'Don't be afraid,' and she was walking through the market-place looking for the box, and her apron did not cover her but nobody noticed, but she was dying of shame. Then she had the box in her hand. She opened it and Manrique's glasses were in it, but they crumbled to powder when she touched them, and he was angry and ran after her, and she screamed with no voice and her feet would not move. And she was running running, trying to catch the glasses, but they danced before her like a feather in the wind, like the wafer, like the bird. And she ran down the aisle of the church and flew up over the altar to the window, and the hypnotist was standing there with the box in his hand, and whirling it round and round, and she began to whirl with it like a pinwheel, through whirling blackness with a thunder in her ears — *you must go to school, Ofelia, you must go to school.*

The doctor came and examined the children while the women looked on silently. 'Warmth,' he said. 'Warmth.' The damp and the cold would be fatal. There was a great scurrying around while the women built a little fireplace of bricks in the room where the children lay, and the beds were remade with sheets and blankets that Lutzie brought.

'I have been busy since the storm,' Doctor González said, when we were walking in the fresh night air. 'Our people are not prepared for cold weather. They are not prepared for anything. In three of the poor families that I take care of, already there have been deaths.'

It was Lupita who died in the Escoto family, though she seemed to have been getting better more quickly than Ofelia. I had gone away to Ixmiquilpan for a few days, and did not know about it until I returned. There was a wreath and a white ribbon on the door of the hut.

Lutzie said they had kept the body until one could not pass the hut, because they hoped that Señor Escoto would return in time to see it. But he had not come, and the Germans and Manolo and other people on the block had insisted on the funeral. I could imagine how the funeral had been, because there is a high death-rate in Mexico, and the funerals of the poor are always part of the city's traffic. It was probably a pullman funeral. The mourners sit all in one bus, and, except that there is no sign of gaiety in their faces, one might think they are going on some excursion beyond the city. No gaiety and no grief. The mourners sit stolidly looking out on the streets, and perhaps they cannot help thinking how strange and wonderful the streets seem, viewed from this brief vantage of the funerary bus. It speeds to the cemetery, and the whole thing cannot take more than a few whisking moments. And thus, with dispatch, they bury their dead.

Ofelia said they had taken Lupita to the pantheon of Dolores. The graves in that cemetery are only rented, and when the time expires a payment must be made or the body is disinterred. The papers make a great scandal about the disinterred bodies. 'It would have been better in my tierra,' Ofelia said. 'It is cheaper there.'

Now they talked often of going back to their tierra. Señor Escoto had returned with news of Daniel. Ofelia did not know what it was, but she said confidently, 'He will be back very soon now. And when he comes we will return to Atotonilco.' She sighed and added: 'It seems we are not for the city. Much has befallen us here.' An air of quiet sadness hung over the lot, but from the Reforma and the neighboring streets came the echo of drums and bugle calls, which seemed like a martial farewell for poor little Lupita. It was the week of the fiestas patrias, the national holidays that commemorate the independence uprising of 1810. The city was bedecked with flags and colored lights, workers and soldiers were parading, and the campesinos were streaming in from the countryside by the thousands. There would be a celebration in the Great Plaza on the night of September 16, with fireworks and cannons and the ringing of the independence bell exactly on the stroke of eleven — the same hour when it was rung over a century ago by the priest Hidalgo, in the little parish of Dolores. But Ofelia would not see any of the parades. 'My mother has forbidden it, señora. She says I must keep off the streets now because there are so many federals around.' She always called a soldier a federal, and ran from one in fear. *Because the federals came from one side and the rebels came from the other, and there was much shooting* . . . So I could not take her to the parades, nor to the celebration in the plaza. But I went with Manrique and we fought our way through the crowds, and heard the bell and saw the fireworks, and bought false noses and the snakes that blow out suddenly and frighten you. The man who sold them said they were 'mother-in-law frighteners.'

'But my mother is very nice,' Manrique said, resuming an old theme. 'You would not have to frighten her.'

'No, Manrique, no. It cannot be,' I answered. 'Besides, I am in love with a mordelon.' He looked at me queerly.

I saw very little of the Escotos now. The women were silent when I came, and I could not help a feeling of guilt. If only I had insisted that the doctor come again, or if I had let Lupita stay in my apartment, warm and dry, instead of worrying that it would interfere with the intelligence tests. By now I had developed a great indifference to the I.Q.'s of the Otomís, though it was not entirely because of Lupita. Having proved that the Otomís react as intelligently in the tests as other races do, only that they react more slowly, I felt that there was no conclusion to be drawn — unless, of course, the obvious conclusion that more time must be allowed for Otomí reaction. Which brings us, if not to a vicious circle, at least to an inane one.

I had undertaken the testing to begin with only at the persuasion of Señor R—— of the Department of Indigenous Affairs. He is a great admirer of the Americans. We are a wonderful people, scientific in everything, and in our zeal for objective knowledge we do not spare even that imponderable quality called intelligence. He considers the I.Q. one of our great inventions, and, astute politician that he is, he apparently felt it would be most impressive to his superiors to show them this scientific folderol of the tests, and also very impressive and pleasing to visiting North-American educators. And he would write, as he later did, in the Department's annual report: 'We are elaborating new scientific tests for the measurement of the intelligence of our indigenous groups, with a view to greater exactitude in the planning of pedagogic programs —'

Irrelevant pomposities, jargon borrowed from the visiting North-American educators, and a foreign language to Mexico. For the Mexican realities are different from ours. Our educational thought, product of our prosperity, is concerned with polishing, refining, and adorning the educational process. Our educators speak a highly intellectualized language, made up of abstract ideas and occupational technicalities — a language that is often pure nonsense, and that has very little content when it is not nonsense. Our education is remote from the real processes

and needs of our society, it has lost its way; and our
educators, like poets in a period of decadence, waste themselves in preciousness and in subtleties and figures of
speech. But meanwhile our prestige is such that there is
a flow of translated pamphlets to our Latin-American
neighbors, about the methods of this or that private school
in some prosperous suburb in Connecticut; about some
pedagogic experiment much bedeviled with scientific
checks and counter-checks. It is rarefied useless manna
to lands that are literally parching with thirst, where the
elementary needs of water and food and shelter and
clothing must yet be conquered. Let us stop sending
them the intellectual waste-products of our abundance,
and really try to understand them.

Of course, it is not all black and white here or in
Mexico; but that is how I felt, working on the report of
'los intelligence tests.' There are some words that Mexicans rarely translate, I suppose because they regard them
as inviolately North-American, the pure essence of our
culture. They talk of 'los go-getters,' 'el noqueout,' 'el
record' (as in drinking more beer than anyone else, or
eating a greater number of apple pies), and 'los intelligence
tests.'

But there were some facts still missing for my paper —
question of correlating race and juvenile delinquency —
and I was to get them from Señor Gómez of the Tribunal
for Minors. Like all Mexican officials sought out by in-
vestigating Americans, he welcomed me with great courtesy and put himself at my service. Then I waited for the
inevitable apologies. Mexicans understand that Americans
are ravenous for documents, studies, statistics — conclu-

sions in handy pill form. But documents, studies, and
statistics are rare in Mexico. The rage for research into
social questions — all that mass of paper work which in
the United States is sometimes necessary, sometimes
merely stupid narcissism, and sometimes dishonest special
pleading — has not yet attacked Mexico. So that usually
you are sent from one office to another, and each time an
elderly gentleman, with a beard more splendid than the
one before, rises from a desk and says, 'Yes, we have
nothing — Sí, no hay nada.' But Señor Gómez was very
proud. In the Tribunal for Minors they had a medico-
pedagogico-psychiatric department, very well documented.
I could look through bulging case histories if I wished —
and he slapped the pile on his desk. But frankly, and
here he lapsed into the natural Mexican, he would rather
talk to me about the work or have me see it in action.
'Then it's very simple,' he said. 'You observe and form
the conclusions indicated.'

And before I could choose, I was seated next to his desk,
to observe the tribunal in action. Five delinquent boys
stood before him, in the blue overalls that they receive
on entering the tribunal. They were misshapen rachitic-
looking youngsters, with the brush-like hair of the mentally
defective. Their faces showed neither fear nor uneasiness
nor guilt, only passive endurance of their days. Señor
Gómez called for their case histories, gave the folders a per-
functory glance, and then shoved them aside. 'Hombre! . . .
Man!' he said, looking at the boys with genuine irritation.
'What did you come back for? What have you been up to
now?' The boys started to explain, while their judge got
up and paced back and forth, sat down, got up again and

leaned against the desk, kneading his chin. The boys went on explaining, and soon everyone was gesticulating with all the eloquence of a family quarrel. Gómez reasoned with them, argued, cajoled — completely absorbed as if he had his own delinquent offspring before him. I would not say that this is the best form of social work, but certainly it is a possible form.

One of the boys had stolen seven pairs of glasses and given a pair to each of the others to sell in the Plaza. You can buy anything that way. The boy runs beside you, holding up a fountain-pen or a wallet or a cigarette-case like bait to lead you on. 'Please, señora, buy it,' he whines. 'Please, señora, I have only one, it is my brother's. Buy it, señora, that I may buy myself something to eat.'

'And you!' Gómez turned indignantly to the oldest boy. 'Didn't you know when you saw the seven pairs of glasses that they were stolen?'

'No, señor.'

'Does your friend here ever wear glasses?'

'No, señor.'

'And yet you thought that he suddenly needed seven pairs?'

They smiled slowly, and Señor Gómez sat back, shaking his head. 'A fine business, a fine business.'

Then he turned to me. 'You must forgive me, señorita, that I am so upset. But we judges are here in lieu of father and mother. Most of these boys, as you see, are neglected. They have no homes, or what they have of one does not deserve the name. This one here' — he shook his pencil at the smallest boy — 'gave as his address a certain number on the Calle de Argentina. We investigated and found it was the site of a junk-pile. Actually, his parents had lived there, but they disappeared, and also the hovel that served them for shelter. But the boy came back with the instinct of a cat and slept there every night. And you —' He turned to another of the boys. 'Are you with your parents again?'

'No, señor, I have left them.'

'And where do you stay?'

'In a hotel, señor.'

'You live there?'

'No, señor. I sleep there. Back of the Hotel Lido, in an alley.' He pointed with his chin at the pile of case histories. 'It's my new address. Put it down.'

The boys filed out with more animation than they had shown when they came in. At least it had been a catharsis. They had laughed and talked and known the intimacy of a paternal scolding. But their judge sighed.

'You Americans are very wise in these things,' he said, 'very advanced. Here we are beginning, and we must learn from you. But look you! Here we are very different. The mind' — he tapped his forehead, for the Mexican gesture is always a pantomime of the words spoken — 'the *mind* is different! We are informal, no? I should be sitting on a bench, high up' — he indicated height — 'and looking down on the boys, no? Pues ...' He shrugged and disposed briskly of the case histories and summoned a young man who had been waiting in the corner. 'The next case will interest you. You will learn much of our Mexican psychology.'

The young man was a lawyer, and Gómez greeted him with a sarcasm I was supposed to admire. 'So, licenciado!

So we are to try this case on legal grounds! Our client
has a lawyer, eh? And the law says this and that...'
He turned to me and continued in a very loud whisper:
'In the time of the fourth viceroy the Mexicans sent a
petition to the Spanish Crown begging that no more
lawyers be sent to New Spain. Mind you! In the time
of the fourth viceroy! Already there were too many
lawyers in Mexico. Well, señor licenciado, and where is
your client?'

The client had disappeared. He had been seen in the
building in the morning, but for some reason or other he
had disappeared.

'The father too?'

'That's it. The father and the son. They both were
here, they poked their heads into the room, and then they
disappeared.'

Señor Gómez drummed on the table, looked at the
clock and reached a decision. 'Well, in any case it is
lunch-time. Have your clients here tomorrow, licenciado,
without fail — the father and the son, and the girl and
her mother too, including that — that' — his hands
scooped the air — 'that little entity which is the where-
fore of the present disturbance.'

The lawyer smiled joylessly and gathered up his papers.
Court was adjourned, and I went out, down the wide
stairway and through the broad patio, to the wrought-
iron doors that were open to the sunny street without
guards. The colonial mansions that the conquerors built
serve the Mexicans well now for public buildings. They
are light and spacious, and the communal center of the
patio is splendid for frescoes. The boys who were interned

in the tribunal were eating at tables in the patio. They must stay in the tribunal three weeks, under observation, until a decision is reached as to where they should be sent. In Tlalpan and Tacubaya, once flourishing centers of Aztec culture and now suburbs of the city, there are homes for delinquent minors. While I had been at the tribunal, a young man had come in and asked that he be sent back to one of these homes. 'It is best for me,' he said. 'It is best for us,' he added, 'for us who have no other remedy in life.'

Daniel

THE FATHER
and the son who had disappeared were Daniel and Señor
Escoto. When I arrived at the tribunal the next morning,
they were both there, standing in front of the desk.

'We have been waiting for you,' Gómez said briskly,
getting me seated. 'I should like you to observe this case
closely, because it is very typical of our Mexicans. This
boy here —' He signaled his assistant to bring the case
history.

Daniel grinned at me unembarrassed, but his father
leaned across the desk, timidly pleading. 'If you please,
Señor Judge, the lady and I are neighbors. It is not right
that she should know of this. If you please...' He fell
silent, looking down and turning his hat in his hand,
while the judge studied the case history. 'Pues... let her

stay,' he said after a while, softly, as if to himself. 'Let her stay — now that she has seen us. That she does not go away thinking it was a robbery or a homicide, or something more evil than it is.'

The lawyer came in with a briefcase, and then a young girl and her mother entered. Daniel and the girl exchanged glances — hers defiant, his amused with a superior male amusement. She was a very pretty young girl.

'Good!' Gómez leaned back, whirling a pencil in his hand while he contemplated Daniel and the girl. 'You two, do you know each other?'

'Pero un momento, hágame el favor — the legal points!' The lawyer flourished his brief, but Señor Gómez waved it away impatiently, and he continued waving it away throughout the trial, and each time I thought how he was simply tossing out all the hard-earned pesos that Daniel's father must have paid for the lawyer's services. Or was it true, after all, that the robbery at the licenciado's...

'Of course I know this girl,' Daniel was saying. 'Everybody knows her —'

'O señor! That you listen to me!' the girl burst out. 'He is lying. He calumniates me. He is a shameless one.'

The judge looked at her rebukingly, and then lifted his thumb and forefinger. The signal meant ahorita — 'a little now.' (In a little now you will be permitted to talk.) It is one of the commonest gestures in the Mexican's vast repertory of sign language, and it may be varied by bringing the thumb and forefinger closer together, when it means 'a very little now.' And then, if it is the waitress in a restaurant who thus signals to you, you may be sure that you have only another half-hour to wait before the food is brought to you.

'Here you have our Mexicans,' Gómez said in an aside to me. 'Lacking in discipline, in that marvelous discipline of you North-Americans.' Then he turned to Daniel again. 'Very well, now. How long have you known this girl?'

'Pues . . .' Daniel folded his arms and put one leg forward, assuming the posture of a man prepared to defend himself, but bored by the necessity. 'Know that the boss sends me often to the outskirts of the city, there where the canal is, to the kiln to make purchases of bricks which are needed in the houses under construction yonder, in the colonia Cuatemoc street of Atoyac, where I myself had employment, or did have until recently, before this woman here deprived me of my senses —'

'Please, young man — the facts!'

'It's a fact,' Daniel shrugged. 'This woman here —'

'Ay, señor, that you hear me!' the girl's mother interrupted. 'Is it just that he calumniate my daughter? Does the law allow it? No, the shoe is on the other foot. We are decent people . . .'

I looked at Daniel's father. He stood looking down, turning his hat in his hand in deep abstraction, as though remote from all that was being said. Was he thinking that it had been wrong for them to leave their tierra and come to the city? All the evil that had befallen them! Lupita . . . and now Daniel. But did not death exist in his tierra, too? And were there not young girls everywhere to deprive a man of his senses? All the evil . . . all the evil. He sighed and looked up. 'If you please, Señor Judge, that we do not make a long thing of this. The boss is waiting for me.'

'Certainly, but still we must have the facts. Now, young man, that you give us the facts.'

'Precisely!' Daniel smiled, shifting his posture. 'As I was saying ... it happens or it did happen that very frequently I used to go beyond the city, to the kiln for a purchase of bricks, a journey sufficiently long so that I was obliged to take the bus —'

Gómez lifted a warning finger. 'What is pertinent, young man.'

'But it is pertinent, señor. You wish me to tell how I came to know this girl?'

'That is the point.'

'Very well. I am telling you.'

'Then proceed to tell me.'

'That is what I am doing.'

'Then please do so.'

'Certainly. With your permission, señor. As I was saying ... it occurred one day that I was waiting for the bus there near the canal, and the girl was waiting there too, and as it happened that the bus delayed a long time, we looked at each other frequently, and then it occurred that we were talking to each other concerning this very matter of the bus. And as the bus continued to delay — well, we did not lack time for talking, as a result of which I learned where she lived and a few other matters which certainly she would not have told me if she had not wished to see me again. For from the very beginning, señor —'

'Mire usted! What is pertinent!'

'Yes, señor. Very well, then. As I was saying, the girl told me where she lived, and one day being in the vicinity again, and wishing to verify the address — out of mere curiosity, you understand, to learn if she had dealt with me honorably or had merely been making sport of me, as happens very often in these matters — well, I directed my steps toward her house, which I found without difficulty, for it is the only house between the canal and Guadalupe, but nearer to Guadalupe, so that it is not too far to walk there. Which is also pertinent, señor, with your permission. For I figured it out ... I would knock at the door and say I was on my way to Guadalupe to see the Virgin. And since I am not from these parts and have never seen her, what more natural than that I should be going to see her? And I had, moreover, the bag which the girl had given me that day of the bus to help me in carrying the things which I had purchased there on my way to the kiln. And I would say that I had stopped in to return it as I was going to Guadalupe, though actually it was a thing of no value and we had not arranged that I should return it. So, as I was saying, I went to the house and knocked and the mother came to the door. "She is not at home," she said. "She has gone to Guadalupe to see the wedding." "Well, I am going to Guadalupe myself," I said, "and as I wish to return this bag to her ..." "You can leave it here," the mother said, and took it from me. And as the mother stood watching me when I left, I was obliged indeed to go to Guadalupe, though actually it was necessary for me to go to the kiln to arrange for another purchase of bricks.'

So he struck out across the fields. The earth was muddy and the walking slow, and the sun was pleasantly warm; so that he had no desire to hurry, but strolled with his hands in his pockets, walking on the yielding earth. And he thought also that thus, by not hurrying, he might meet her returning through the fields. Beyond he could see the towers of Guadalupe, with the Cathedral rising on a hill

over the purple-dark trees and the white houses. The
dome of it was a golden glory in the sun and around it
clustered the domed chapels, golden too, and nearer there
was a line of tall poplars that marked the highway. They
said there would soon be a new highway going past Guadalupe to join the great road that went to the United States,
and they said that people earned a great deal of money
in the United States. He would go there sometimes, because he was a man for travel and for studying strange
things. He would go to Michigan and New York and he
would come back to his pueblo wearing an American shirt
and an American hat, and telling everyone of the wonders
he had seen over there.

And thinking of these things he came to the town. But
by now it was past noon and there was no use in turning
back to the kiln because nobody would be there. So he
walked through the streets of Guadalupe, and he remembered that the girl had gone to the Cathedral to see
the wedding. He thought that he might go there too and
find her. And if not he would see the Virgin whom he had
long wanted to see, the most famous Virgin in all Mexico.
It was like a holy day inside the Cathedral, with all the
people who had come to see the wedding; and the air
was heavy with the perfume of flowers and there was a
glory of lights, and everyone was pressing toward the altar
to see the richly dressed wedding guests, and the soldiers
who were waiting with their swords ready to form an
arch for the bride and bridegroom. He walked around
looking for the girl and once he thought he saw her, kneeling with a candle in her hand. But it wasn't she, and there
were so many people that he knew he would not find her.

And then he went looking for the Virgin and found her in a splendid altar of marble and gold, and he knelt down and looked up at her; but all the time thinking of the girl whom he could not drive from his mind because he was obsessed with this desire to see her. And he was ashamed to be thinking of the girl and praying to the Virgin at the same time, and so he went out of the church in order that he might think of her without sacrilege, and he walked through the market...

'Please, señor, will you tell me — was it in Guadalupe that you met the girl again?'

'I am telling you, señor. It was not in Guadalupe.'

'Then will you tell me where it was?'

'Certainly. I am coming to that. As I was saying, being obsessed with the idea of seeing her...'

'You were obsessed?'

'Yes, señor, I was obsessed...'

He could not sleep that night for thinking of the girl, and in the days that followed he could not rid himself of the desire to see her. It was a fever and a thirst, and he was like one possessed. So one day he went to her house again, but this time he went boldly without excuses. But again she was not there and the mother stood at the door watching him as he went away. So that there was no way of waiting for the girl, unless he were to come back and hide in the ditch beyond the house, which would be to make himself ridiculous. So he walked along the canal wondering how he could contrive to meet her, and then an idea occurred to him and he went back and entered a store which was on the canal, but still within sight of the house. He ordered a refresco and while he drank it, he asked: 'To whom do those horses in the field belong?'

'Naturally, to the Señor Licenciado Don Carlos Rosales de la Selva,' said the man. 'They are his horses.'

'I suppose he has someone to care for them?'

'Naturally. Alfredo takes care of them.'

'Ah ... then there is no need of my applying. I am experienced with horses. I was a stable boy in my tierra.'

'No, there is no need.'

'But Alfredo lives in that house?'

'He lives there. He is a bachelor.'

'Strange ... I saw a woman there as I passed.'

'That is his sister. He lives with his sister and her daughter. They are former servants of the señor, and therefore he permits them to stay there.'

'That is very kind of him.'

'Certainly it is kind, for they are very poor. But then they care for the chickens and the girl brings the little white ones to the señor. Just this morning she went with a basketful of them.'

'Then it is not far where the señor lives?'

'No farther than Tacubaya.'

He finished his refresco and went out, and then he went to Tacubaya and found the house and waited outside, never looking away from the gates; for it was a great house behind gardens and trees and there were several gates, and he was afraid he would not see the girl coming out. And at last he saw her, leaving with the basket in which she had carried the eggs, and he spoke to her and he was beside himself with joy at seeing her; but angry also for the pain she had caused him. And in his anger and joy he said foolish things — called her his heart and his life and other endearments, and he would not let her go until she had consented to go with him to the fair in Tacubaya, that night on the Feast of Saint Joseph.

'And in this manner,' said Daniel, 'as I have just explained, the girl and I became sweethearts.'

'O señor, he is lying. We never became sweethearts, for that was never in his mind. Ask him, do me the favor to ask him if that was ever in his mind. It was only, "Please, Luisita!" "Luisita, I want you!" "Luisita, I am dying!" A shameless thing, without sentiment or delicacy.'

'You are sure of that? Because this of being sweethearts is a serious matter.'

'Certainly it is serious. And therefore I tell you, there never was any talk of that. He never even gave me his picture, señor. You may see in my house there is no picture of him.'

Daniel snorted. 'And how if she had destroyed the picture?'

'Please, young man, that you allow me to question the witness!' He shook his pencil at the girl. 'You would say, then, that you felt for him only the sentiment of friendship?'

'Señor, it was a thing like this. He followed me and followed me there in Tacubaya, and in Guadalupe and wherever I went. Wherever I turned he was there, begging me: "Please, Luisita, I am going crazy." "Just one more time, Luisita, once more and then I will leave you alone." So that each time I took pity on him, and I spoke to him out of pity, seeing him so obsessed . . .'

'Ah . . . one moment. Then we may say that out of pity you were obliged to give yourself to him too?'

The girl colored and did not answer, and Daniel looked

at her smiling, very male and amused. 'Ay, Luisita,' he
said, 'how you lie! It grieves me the way you are lying.
Then you don't remember those nights in Tacubaya...'

'Please, young man, I must forbid you to address the
witness.' Gómez leaned back, stroking his chin while he
looked from Daniel to the girl. Then he looked at the case
history, and then he looked at the girl and at Daniel again.

'With your permission, Señor Judge ...' The lawyer
came forward, holding his brief determinedly. 'If we have
finished with the sentimentalities, with your permission...'

'Certainly. That we hear from the law!'

'If you had read my brief, the point is simple. The girl
is pregnant and fixes the responsibility on this boy. Yet
in so far as there is a doubt about the girl's morality —
that is to say, no proof positive that there were not others
with whom she had relations — and certainly it is obvious
that the girl went very willingly, that is to say, there was
a lack of morality on both sides...'

Señor Gómez winced with closed eyes, as one who hears
chalk rasping on a blackboard.

'Licenciado,' he said, 'will you do me a favor?'

'If it is possible, Señor Judge.'

'Will you stop braying?'

'If the judge is pleased to make sport of this —'

'No, it is you who are making sport of this. Because the
matter is serious, more serious than you lawyers in your
legal myopia will ever see. But I who sit here day after
day and see the homeless children that come to this desk,
children of unions such as this one we have here, I believe
I am in a position to know how serious it is. You mention

the lack of a sense of responsibility, and I say: Precisely. That is what we Mexicans suffer from, that is the great sickness of Mexico. And I say we must fight it, and I say the boy must be held responsible. Do you understand what I mean by responsible? In his heart, Señor Licenciado.'

'Sentimentalities, Señor Judge. According to the law —'

'Vaya! The law! That doesn't enter here, but I'll tell you what does. Tell me, how many homeless children are there in our city of Mexico?'

'I would be very pleased if you told me, Señor Judge.'

'Qué va, that I must tell you! When the shame of it is known to all of us. And you wish to add another?'

'And the boy must be made the scapegoat?'

'He must be taught, as all our young men of Mexico must be taught.'

'Sociology, señor.'

'As you wish to call it.'

'Pues, if your mind is made up . . .'

Daniel's father leaned across the desk. 'If you please, Señor Judge, the boss is waiting for me. If the judge will only say, anything that he wishes me to do . . .'

'Yes, now we have talked enough.' The girl's mother nodded at him approvingly, and adjusted her rebozo in readiness to leave. 'Speak, Señor Judge! That the boy pay for the expenses of the baby.'

But the judge, looking at the case history, signaled 'a little now,' and everyone waited. 'One thing more,' he said, turning the pages. 'To fix the date, for the dates must coincide. How long has the girl been pregnant?'

'A matter of seven months, señor.'

'And you would say it began on the Feast of Saint Joseph?' He turned to Daniel.

'I would say that, señor, for on that day . . .'

They were walking through the fair, and the place was a blaze of colored lights, and there was music and fireworks, and they had bought bags of confetti and ridden on the carrousel; and now they were strolling past the booths and looking at the things to buy, and at the little clay ducks that people were shooting at. And Daniel held her close, and it was late and they did not want to go home.

'Is there anything else you want, Luisita?'

'No, we have done everything.'

'Yes, but can't you think of something else?'

'Of what?'

'I don't know. Something else that might please you. They say there are horses for riding.'

'Ah, in my tierra how I used to ride!'

'Then let us look for the horses.'

'No, I am tired.'

'You are scared.'

'Qué va! If I have ridden the wildest! I would whisper to the horse in his ear with affection, and then he understood me and I was never afraid.'

'I would like to see you ride, Luisita.'

'Here in the city one cannot. It is not a modest thing here. It is only for making a show of oneself like the charras.'

'I will buy you a charra costume. I take it on myself to buy it. A long skirt with silver bangles.'

'Such nonsense, Daniel. I would be ashamed to wear it.'

'And then you will have your picture taken and give it to me.'

'Yes, I have been thinking of that.'

'Thinking of what, Luisita?'

'That I would go to the Alameda and have my picture taken.'

'Then I think you must have a sweetheart.'

'The things you imagine!'

'Yes, you have a sweetheart in your tierra. Why did you deceive me? I am going to your tierra to fight with him. I will challenge him. I will have it out with him. Tell me: what is he called and how does he look? Is he handsomer than I?'

'You are making fun of me, Daniel. I swear that I have no sweetheart.'

'And this of the picture?'

'I was only thinking of it.'

'But for me, Luisita, not for that other one in your tierra.'

'But there is no other one, Daniel. You will see, I will give you my picture.'

'Do you promise it?'

'Yes, tomorrow I will go to the Alameda.'

'No, we will go to Xochimilco. We will go on a Sunday.'

'On Sunday I cannot. We have promised to hear a Mass for the repose of my father.'

'That cannot take the whole day. We will go after the Mass.'

'If my mother allows it. She does not approve of excursions.'

'I will speak to your mother. I take it on myself to speak to her. You will see.'

'Just imagine, I have never been to Xochimilco.'

'Nor to the Castle either?'

'Not there either.'

'Nor to the Desert of the Lions?'

'Even less.'

'Then I think you know very little of the city. Here we are in the metropolis and you do not know the things that there are for diversion.'

'And you — have you seen so much?'

'I am newly arrived. I have not had time. But I think of going to Xochimilco, and to the Desert of the Lions, and to the Convent of Acolman —'

'Then go. There is no problem.'

'But these are not places for seeing alone.'

'Then you lack for women?'

'No, no lack of that. But how if one should please me more than another?'

'Ah . . . then you have a sweetheart.'

'No, I swear it. It is you who have a sweetheart. There in your tierra.'

'How jealous you are! I am afraid of you, Daniel. How you frightened me today when I came from the house, after leaving the little white ones. Ay, Daniel! How you follow me!'

'Because I love you, Luisita.'

'You are raving and I do not believe it.'

'Do not believe it, but I say that I love you.'

'Look, there are drops of rain.'

'Yes, it is beginning to rain.'

'Let us go, they are waiting for me.'

'Look, Luisita. That you do not go home tonight —'

'No, they are waiting for me and it is beginning to rain.'

'Here ... there is no rain here. Stand close, Luisita, come under my jacket.'

'Ay, Daniel! What do you want of me? I am afraid ...'

'I want to please you, niñita. You will see. You will see how I will please you and you will not be afraid.'

'You follow me and follow me! I am afraid of you, Daniel. I think you will do me an injury. I think you will kill me.'

'No, I will please you, Luisita. How I will please you! My heart and my life, my lovely little heaven, how I will please you!'

They stood under the awning and the rain came down and they could not see the lights of the fair. Some musicians came out of the cantina. 'What do we play you?' they called mockingly, seeing Daniel and the girl. Then they ran through the rain, bent over, protecting their instruments. 'I will please you. My heart and my life, lovely little heaven, how I will please you ...'

'Then it was there in Tacubaya, on the Feast of Saint Joseph?' said Señor Gómez.

'It was there,' Daniel answered, 'and after that the girl did not want to go back to the mother, so that we were obliged to stay in Tacubaya, until the failure of money caused her to return to the mother, after which I saw her with less frequency and with great difficulty, considering the watchfulness of the mother. But the first night, certainly, was there in Tacubaya on the Feast of Saint Joseph —'

'Señor, he held me! He would not let me go. It was only out of fear, señor! Because of the wild things he said — of how he would kill me if I did not stay with him.'

Daniel folded his arms and looked at her, sadly patient. 'And it was fear afterward, too, then? When you followed me, Luisita? Yes, ask her, señor! That she tell you how, when I had tired of the thing — how she pursued me and came to me there where I was watching at night at the building on Atoyac, and molested me that I should go with her, and moreover because of this matter of the baby ... So that I was obliged to abandon my employment and go with her, and since, as it happens, I have a sweetheart and not wishing any of this to come to her ears ...'

Señor Gómez threw his pencil down triumphantly, as one who reaches the solution of a difficult equation. 'There, you see, licenciado? There's your proof positive. The boy is compromised with one girl and goes off with another. Lack of responsibility, and therefore I say —'

The lawyer shrugged, threw up his hands, and Gómez leaned back to announce his decision while the mother nodded approvingly: 'Yes, Señor Judge, that the boy pay for the expenses of the baby. Nothing more.' She figured it out. It came to sixty pesos.

There were formalities. Señor Gómez lectured Daniel on his conduct, and made the girl promise that she would keep the baby and care for it. Then Daniel's father counted out the sixty pesos, and put it on the desk, and Señor Gómez gave it to the girl's mother. 'And you two'— he looked at Daniel and the girl. 'That you refrain from molesting each other in the future.' He was very severe about this.

'Naturally,' said Daniel's father. 'Why should they see

one another, now that the thing is settled and the boy is
to be married? Pues...' He shrugged away such possi-
bilities.

Then they went out, the girl and her mother first,
Daniel and his father following at a decent distance. But
the girl kept looking back at Daniel, and the mother had
to nudge her angrily to make her come.

And Another Wedding

ND so there would be a wedding. One morning I looked down on the lot and saw a man weaving a rebozo — a very long one of fine black wool — for Daniel's sweetheart. The man worked standing up, with one end of his loom tied to a tree and the other end tied around his waist; and everyone stood watching, while he threw the shuttle and changed the threads, silent and absorbed in his work. I had never had a desire to buy the artifacts of Mexico and take them home; but I found myself wanting that rebozo. For it would always have in it the skillful movements of the man's hands, and the absorbed contemplation of those who stood watching, and the long golden hours of the morning in which it was woven. But it was for Daniel's sweetheart. When the year was over, they would cele-

brate the wedding, and then the Escotos would return
to their tierra.

'My mother says, come with us to Atotonilco,' Ofelia
pleaded. 'Our home there is very humble, but if it should
please you to stay with us awhile ...'

'No, I too must return to my tierra.'

'So far away?' she said.

'As far as it must be,' I answered, with Mexican resignation.

'And you won't forget to send me the picture of the
building which is over a hundred stories high?'

'I won't forget.'

'But don't expect me to believe it,' she warned. 'No,
such things are not to be believed.'

It was Christmas time, a Christmas of blue skies and
warm sunny days, a period of fiestas when little work
was done on the buildings. There was talk now that all
the work on the buildings would soon be over. Whole
blocks of new houses had been built, but now it was coming to an end. There would be no more work for the peons
and all the families would have to move. Already there
was a busyness of departure in the huts — a frenzy of
clothes-washing and pot-scrubbing, an airing of all the
sarapes and straw sleeping mats. It was festive and sad
at the same time; for though the huts had been poor
shelter at best, nobody wanted to leave them. But it
had been illegal for the families to be living on the lot
without water and sanitation, and now that the peons
were no longer needed, the company remembered the
illegality. And the families were told to go.

'Pues, it seems it is the law,' Señor Escoto said. 'For
that there is no remedy.'

It was the night of Daniel's wedding and we were sitting in the hut waiting for him, so that the wedding might begin. It would be a very simple wedding. Señor Escoto had bought tequila, and the people of the huts would come and join in the drinking. But Daniel delayed, and there were long pauses in the conversation, while the women stared at the door, wondering why he did not come. 'DANIEL!' It was Ofelia's voice ringing sharp and clear, just once far away. 'She is calling him,' said Mrs. Escoto; and then, in the moment of silence after she spoke, we heard the scream. It was a high deliberate scream, almost as if someone had tried to sing on a note beyond range of the voice; then it was repeated, only this time the high pitch fell on a long-drawn downward shudder, agonizing and inhuman. And then the silence of the night outside the hut was louder, so loud that it seemed as if the air thundered together after the sound had rent it.

Daniel's sweetheart spoke first, drawing her rebozo around her face, pale as death. 'Daniel!'

'That you don't go, I tell you! That you don't go!' She had rushed blindly to the door, holding her arms before her as if to ward off a blow. But Señor Escoto held her, caught her uplifted arms and struggled with her. 'That you don't go, I tell you!'

'Let me go, let me go!' she cried.

The door opened on the blue quiet night, and she was gone, running toward the place where the scream had come from. But by now everyone was on the street, and Manolo and Edouardo came from the store, and everyone stood looking down the street where there was nothing but her tall running figure and a solitary lamp splashing light on her as she passed.

'It is she,' Manolo said; 'the insane one who tried to throw herself from the building today.'

'None other,' Edouardo affirmed. 'All day she went through the streets like one insane, and she went up on all the buildings where the peons were working, and they said to her: "Get out, woman. Don't you know you are not permitted here?" "Does Juan work here?" she asked. "What Juan?" they said. Well, you know there is always a Juan on the buildings, so finally they said, "Yes, he works here." "Let me speak to him," she said. "Let me go up and speak to him." "Why do you want to speak to him?" they said. "He owes me money," she said. "Let me go up and speak to him." And then, because she behaved like one insane, they said: "It is not allowed to go up. You may speak to him when the peons leave." "And when do they leave?" she asked. "At seven," they said, and she went away saying she would be back at seven. And she did this over and over like one insane, trying to get to the top of the buildings — that she might hurl herself down.'

'But now, obviously, she has done it,' Manolo concluded.

'Pues . . .' Señor Escoto was lighting a cigarette. The match flared unsteadily in his cupped fingers. 'It is no great matter. She cannot be hurt much, for look you, all the buildings are low.' He threw the match away, pocketed the cigarettes and sauntered off. A few of the men followed him. 'It is no great matter,' he called back negligently, as if already announcing what he had found.

'No, it can be no great matter,' Manolo echoed with authority. 'She will be hurt, nothing more.' He went back to lock the door of the bakery, and the group dissolved

from its frozen compactness. More of the men followed
Señor Escoto, and the women called to the children and
made them stay close, protecting them with their rebozos.

Ofelia's mother stood leaning against the hut, her face
hidden in shadow. 'And you saw her?' she asked of
Edouardo.

'Certainly I saw her. A young woman, very pretty,
but pale pale with this rage to destroy herself. She came
into the store —'

'Ah, you spoke to her?'

'Certainly I spoke to her, for she came into the store.
"What do you wish?" I asked, but she was incapable of
answering, staring at me like one who has taken leave of
her senses. "Is there a Juan here?" she said, indicating
the buildings where the peons were still working —'

'It was Juan she wanted,' Mrs. Escoto mused. 'Juan!
Who would it be, this Juan?'

'Clearly the name of her lover,' the young aunt nodded
wisely.

'Clearly she was a deceived one,' said Edouardo.
'Greatly deceived in love. For this she destroyed herself.'

'Ah ... poor woman, to destroy herself for love.'

'Pues, when one is deceived ...'

We heard the shriek of the siren, and then we saw the
ambulance turning in, far away at the corner where Daniel
had once been watchman.

'That Ofelia!' Mrs. Escoto said irritably. 'Where will
she be?'

After a while we saw her. She came down the dark
street alone, walking as calmly as if she had only been to

market; but with the story on her lips — Daniel's story, though she did not know that, and the story of her own courage, too. She told it over and over, and she told it again when we were sitting in the hut, waiting by candle-light for the return of the others. They had taken Daniel to the police station for questioning, and his sweetheart and Señor Escoto had gone along.

'"That you take me too!" I said, for I saw it all and I know Daniel was not to blame. But imagine, they would not let me go along. They pushed me aside for a little one, and they would not let me go, though I could have told them exactly how it was. She was standing there where it was dark, near the wall, and I noticed it as I passed the first time looking for Daniel. And it must have been a long time she stood there, for when I came back she was just going into the building. I saw it — something black that disappeared into the door, and I thought maybe it was Daniel and I went in, too, but only a little way so as not to lose the light from the street. Sacred heart! What a fright I had when she turned and looked at me, pale as death itself and with two great eyes staring, but silent silent, so that I thought it was a ghost. And then it entered my mind she had come to steal something and they would blame it on Daniel who had been the watch-man there. "What do you want?" I said. "Whom are you looking for?" I said. But she did not answer, only stared at me. Sacred heart, how she looked at me, that my blood stood still! Then she turned and went upstairs and it was dark dark, and I had to feel my way, sliding my hand on the banister and afraid to touch her, because still I was not sure that she was not a ghost. "That you tell me what it is!" I said loudly, but not a word, not a sound; and I crossed myself twice and said a prayer to myself. Then we came to the top of the stairs and she stood a moment holding her hand to her throat. She made a queer sound with her throat, but she was not crying, it was as though she felt pain. And I thought I would faint with fear and I wanted to run down again, but for the fear of turning my back to her, for by now I knew she was a crazy one, from whom there is always great danger.'

'You did wrong,' Mrs. Escoto said severely. 'You did wrong not to call someone. You see?' she turned to me. 'It is always so with the child! Presuming and meddlesome in everything! And how if the woman had really done you an injury?'

'Ah, but since she was bent on destroying herself,' the young aunt mused.

'It entered my mind,' Ofelia continued, unabashed. 'I do not know how, but this very thing entered my mind — that she proposed to destroy herself, and then I felt no fear, but only the thought that she must not do it. We came to the roof and without fear I touched her, but she shook me away, still making that strange sound in her throat, and she walked to the edge, but swiftly swiftly with long strides, and then —'

She could tell it calmly now, though at first she had faltered. There was a moment when everything seemed to happen at once. Ofelia too ran to the edge of the roof, looking down fearfully at the street. She saw Daniel walking on the street, very unconcerned, with his hands in his pockets, and she called in her terror: 'Daniel!'

And just as she called, the woman's scream pierced her ears, and looking around she saw only a great emptiness, the white emptiness of the moonlight, and no sound, no sound, until Daniel came bounding up the stairs.

'I had to shake the child to get the story from her,' Daniel said later. He had been released by the police, for they could find no connection between this act of a crazy woman and the fact that Daniel had once been watchman at the building. 'I had to shake her, for she was standing there crying, and pointing — pointing ...'

And the talk dissolved into censure for Ofelia, who had been presuming and meddlesome again, and so witnessed something it would be better never to have seen. As for the woman, she would not live. She had impaled herself on the spikes next to the building, where they had made forms for pouring cement.

The story became a seven-days' wonder, to be told over and over again to the curious who came to stare at the building. The story of Luisita — poor Luisita who even in her rage to destroy herself had remembered Señor Gómez' last warning: '*That you two do not molest each other.*' And she had gone asking for Juan, and tried to destroy herself near the hut where Daniel might perhaps see her and pity her. And failing that, she had gone to the building, the same place where I had seen them together that night of the fireworks, and where they must have been together many times.

Neither Daniel nor his father ever mentioned her name, and yet I was sure it was Luisita. At times I was sure, and at other times it seemed a mystery. Like the question of the robberies. But whenever I think of the robberies, the memory of Ofelia comes to reproach me. She was sure they were not the work of Daniel or her father, and she was wise in all things.

Dear Ofelia! I was sorry to leave Mexico and I was sorry to leave you, and though we promised to write I have only sent the picture of the building over a hundred stories high. Perhaps it hangs now in the hut and you point to it as evidence of the wonders, the incredible wonders of my tierra. Or have you left the city and gone back to your tierra? I have promised myself to write and find out, and some day I shall, since in this uncertain world somehow the only thing we seem to accomplish is finally to write the long-delayed letters. And I shall address the envelope: 'Señorita Ofelia Escoto, Atotonilco, Jalisco' — adding in the corner, 'The house is known,' which is the way one addresses letters to a village in Mexico.

That time on the trip home, when the bus stopped in the tropics of Jacala... We sat having lunch in the hot shade of the hotel porch, and the musicians came over and the whine of the violins sounded familiar. They played us the song of your tierra. 'In that Atotonilco the orange trees are in flower, the maidens appear like little angels of God...' I was only a few hours away from the house on Atoyac, but already it seemed a long time, and this song of your tierra was a reminder of something far in the past. But how much longer it seems now whenever I am reminded! Here in the cold North there is a man who walks back and forth on the corner near my house. You would laugh to see him wearing a Mexican sombrero, here where there is no sun on the street, where it is cold cold. He carries signs in front and in back printed in big red letters: EAT AT PEDRO'S, MEXICAN CHILE. And he looks very hungry and the signs do not warm him. But whenever I see him I seem to hear again the song of your tierra, and I wonder if I shall find you again when I return to Mexico. Probably I will pass you in the market-place without knowing. You will be like all the others — an anonymous rebozo in the market-place, a maid, as you wished to be, carrying the tortillas for some well-to-do family; and very proud of your servanthood, very pleased to be scrubbing and scouring and fetching and carrying for them. And then you will marry and have many children, *for one goes on having children until the thing finishes itself*. It might have been different if you had gone to school. But that could not be, and perhaps it is just as well, for 'who knows?' I remember how you used to say that, like a Mexican. I remember you whenever I think of Mexico. Dear Ofelia ...